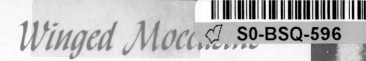

Winged Moccasins

The Story of Sacajawea

by FRANCES JOYCE FARNSWORTH

Illustrated by LORENCE F. BJORKLUND

The beautiful and moving story of a Shoshone Indian girl whose winged moccasins carried her over the shining mountains, the first woman to cross the Rockies, as interpreter and guide for the Lewis and Clark expedition.

Sacajawea was only ten when her father, a Shoshone Chief, was killed by a hostile tribe. She was taken prisoner and sold into slavery. During the next several years she was traded from one tribe to another until, while a slave of the Mandans and still not yet twenty, she attracted the attention of Toussaint Charbonneau, a trapper, and became his wife.

When the Lewis and Clark expedition reached the headwaters of the Missouri, they needed a guide who knew the country and the language of the western tribes. Charbonneau told the explorers about his young wife, and although they did not favor taking a woman on such a dangerous trip, they were so impressed by her bearing, her knowledge of the region and the dialects of the Indians, they decided to take both of them along.

Sacajawea proved an excellent guide—faithful, loyal and indispensable. She secured the friendship of unfriendly Indians and, reunited with her brother, now a Chief of the Shoshones, she was able to secure horses and provisions for the expedition. With her little son Baptiste strapped to her back, she endured the severe hardships of the journey and gained the respect of every man on the expedition. She never complained, for she worshipped Clark who seemed to understand the restlessness within her, the desire for knowledge, the yearning for new places.

When the expedition was over, Sacajawea settled in St. Louis so that Baptiste could attend school, and here she learned French and English, both of which proved valuable in later life when she returned to her own people and became active in Indian affairs.

Throughout the great change when the Indian hunting and camping grounds grew smaller, Sacajawea was an ambassador without portfolio for the white man among her own people to whom she gave wise advice and good counsel. A brave, noble, proud and intelligent woman, she was highly honored by the white man as well as by the Indians, at a time when a squaw had no voice in the Council of Chiefs.

Her winged moccasins finally came to rest when Sacajawea died in her late nineties. Mrs. Farnsworth has written a poignant story that will stir the heart and the emotion of every reader. The beautiful illustrations by Lorence Bjorklund capture the mood and the dramatic impact of the book.

Winged Moccasins

THE STORY OF SACAJAWEA

Winged Moccasins

THE STORY OF
SACAJAWEA

By

Frances Joyce
Farnsworth

ILLUSTRATED BY LORENCE F. BJORKLUND

Julian Messner • New York

JB
S

Published by Julian Messner, Inc.
8 West 40th Street, New York 18
Published Simultaneously in Canada
by The Copp Clark Company, Ltd.
Copyright 1954 by Frances Joyce Farnsworth
Printed in the United States of America

Library of Congress Catalog Card No. 54-6765

3-12-55

TO
my friend
EMMA E. SCHAEFER

Contents

Preface   11

1. The Call of the Wild Geese   13
2. The Hunt   26
3. Taken Captive   33
4. The Camp of the Minataree   38
5. The Pale Face   46
6. The Coming of Lewis and Clark   55
7. Little Pomp   62
8. Hilltops   72
9. A Daring Rescue   79
10. Of the Same Blanket   89
11. The Pacific at Last   104
12. Waiting through a Winter   111
13. Homeward Bound   122
14. Down the Missouri   131
15. White Man's Magic   141
16. A Wanderer   147
17. Life with the Comanches   155
18. The Return to Her People   159
19. Life on the Reservation   167

In Memory   181

Bibliography   183

Index   185

Preface

One hundred years after the Lewis and Clark Expedition it was discovered that Sacajawea, their famous Indian girl guide, had been almost completely lost in oblivion. It was known that she was not yet twenty years of age when she and her French trader husband had left the exploring party on its return. The question arose, how had she spent the remainder of her life and where was she buried? There were many confusing reports and much controversy.

The United States Department of Indian Affairs undertook the task of tracing her lost years and appointed Dr. Charles Alexander Eastman, a Sioux Indian and college graduate, to visit the Shoshones, Minatarees, Mandans, Comanches, and any other tribe where Indians might be living who had known her personally or by tradition. On March 16, 1925, it was declared formally in Washington, D.C., that the grave of Sacajawea was in the Shoshone Wind River Reservation in Wyoming.

Many historians became interested, but no one entered the search more wholeheartedly than, or with such keen interest and true enjoyment as, Dr. Grace Raymond Hebard, Professor of Wyoming History at the University of Wyoming. An account of her search of over thirty years would be a story in itself. With the aid of trained assistants she accumulated a vast storehouse of authentic information from hundreds of sources. Old diaries, books, expense accounts, government records, and letters gave up their clues to lead her on to new sources of information. She went among the Shoshone Indians gathering data firsthand from friends and descendants of the famous Indian woman. Perhaps her greatest thrill was the result of a clue that led her to Germany. Here she employed an archivist who transcribed a travel diary of Prince Paul William of Württemberg containing information that corresponded with what she had gathered from Sacajawea's grandchildren. Her research was conducted entirely separately from Dr. Eastman's; but their results were the same, thus giving double proof to their conclusions.

The data thus collected, though fragmentary and leaving blank spaces of many years, have furnished the framework for *Winged Moccasins*. In it the author has rounded out the facts in accordance with the known information concerning the characters and the customs of that day in order that the reader may have a better understanding of the Indian woman, Sacajawea, whose faithful service is a shining epic in the pages of our nation's history.

Winged Moccasins

THE STORY OF SACAJAWEA

Chapter 1

The Call of the Wild Geese

Sacajawea dug her bare heels into her pony's sides in an effort to increase his speed. The time was short—already the long shadows had reached their full stature as the sun rested upon the mountain rim. She bent forward as she urged him on as if in her eagerness she might help him climb the last steep hill. Her friend, Rabbit Ear, sat behind her clutching Sacajawea's slender waist to steady

13

herself upon the pony's back. "We are almost there," breathed Sacajawea, "almost."

"You are out of breath," complained her friend. "Do you climb the hill, or the pony? Why come here? The hill is so steep."

"We see far from this hilltop. We can see"—and Sacajawea lowered her voice to a whisper—"almost into another world! It is wonderful! Do you not feel it?"

"No," said Rabbit Ear wearily. "Hilltops! Another hilltop! They are food and drink to you. I do not know why." The tired pony climbed the last few steps and Sacajawea cried out with joy. They had reached the top. The mountain range lay before them in full view, its wooded slopes and bare peaks capped with snow.

"The mountains are proud old squaws with snow-white hair gathering their purple robes about them," whispered Sacajawea. Then as the sun dropped from sight behind the mountains its rays rose high into the sky turning the billowing clouds overhead into a fairyland of opalescent beauty. The girls dismounted and stood watching the changing colors.

"The tent flap of the sky opens for the setting sun," said Sacajawea, almost as if she were talking to herself, "and the light from the land beyond the sunset for a moment floods the world."

The colors deepened and the shadows came stealing in to spread the blanket of dusk over all the world as the proud old-lady mountains shrouded themselves more deeply to join the darkness of the night.

"I need your eyes to see it," said Rabbit Ear. "The tent

flaps of the sky! The land beyond! Is what you say true, Sacajawea?"

"You saw the light. Our people say there is a happy hunting ground where we go when we die. Sometimes they say 'the land beyond the sunset.' Perhaps the tent flap opens into that land. I do not know. No one has told me. But I like to think it is so, just as I like to think the little white flowers that bloom on the mountainside in early spring are the spirits of babies and little children coming back to us in this way to make us happy."

Her friend shook her head as they climbed onto the pony and turned toward home.

Home was the camp of her people, a roving band of Shoshone Indians, only a mile or two away. It had been their home for several days now, but tomorrow they might decide to move to a place that the Chief and his leaders believed to be near a more plentiful supply of food. The skin tepees were easy to move and their few belongings light in weight. They moved often. When they camped long in one spot the dust and dirt from the flying feet of shouting, laughing children and barking dogs would rise into a cloud. So a move was as good as a housecleaning, although the Indians did not seem to mind the dirt—they accepted it all with the many other unpleasant things in life.

They kept no record of time, although they recalled tragedies such as terrible storms or defeats at the hands of other Indians by lives—"the life of an old man ago" or "three old men," which would be so far back it would be impossible for them to remember. They did not know their ages. On the day the two girls watched the sunset they must have been twelve or thirteen years of age. They were no longer little children and had already begun to bear the burdens of the life of a squaw, although they were still allowed freedom from tasks when there was no work to be done. There were no skins to prepare for clothing, no food to be dried, so the two friends had enjoyed the long day together. Now the day was over and it was time to go home.

Sacajawea stopped the pony suddenly. She had heard a call—a call that she knew, a call that seemed always to speak to her. She listened breathlessly as it came clear and strong to her ears. Her eyes searched the sky and there, in the gathering dusk, she saw high in the air a vee formation of wild geese flying as they called out their farewell to the land until another springtime. She slipped down from the pony's back. The birds were going far away to a land where there would be warmth and sunshine. If only she could go too! She raised her arms and the wind, which had risen suddenly, blew back the deerskin garment against her slender, girlish figure. Everything was forgotten save the birds overhead, and her voice blended with the wind as she called, "Wait for me, wait for me!" She ran forward as if her longing must in some way give her power to follow them. When they were lost in the shadowy distance and she could no longer hear their call she stood motionless. Suddenly her shoulders seemed to sag and she turned back to the pony and her friend.

"Why do you do this, Sacajawea?" asked Rabbit Ear. "They are only birds. Wild geese. They cannot take you with them. When you hear their call you become another person."

Sacajawea nodded. "When I hear their call I forget everything else. I do not know why. Their call awakens something within me stronger than I."

"You are my friend. I will speak to you. Stop running after birds. Stop climbing hilltops. It is like a fever with you. It is a strange way. There is talk about you. Do you know what the squaws say? They say the name your mother gave you has cast a spell upon you."

"My name has no part of it," answered Sacajawea firmly. "My mother has told me about my name. It is motion. She gave it in the sign language when I was very young. Whether it is of a flying bird or a boat being launched does not matter. I love it. Oh, Rabbit Ear, there is so much I want to know and see! I ask questions in vain. No one will tell me. Where do they go—the birds—and why do they not return until the cold is gone? If they go away from the cold, why do we not go too? But when I ask they laugh. It is a silly question, they say. The birds go—why should I wonder? When I ask what is beyond the sunset, they laugh! When I ask where the rivers go, they laugh! Every time I climb a new hilltop I hold my breath for what I may see beyond. Will there be more beyonds? My questions are foolish; I have a spell upon me—that is my answer. It does not destroy my longing. It is a part of me. It is strong. It beats within me like the wings of a trapped bird. Someday I will follow the birds and the streams and I shall find out all these things for myself."

"I believe you will," her friend answered. "I shall not be with you, but I will miss you."

The pony picked his way gingerly down the steep slope and out to the trail that led to the camp. They jogged along in silence. Rabbit Ear was the first to speak. "They hunt again tomorrow. I hope they bring home meat. I am tired of roots and berries."

"They must," said Sacajawea. "If we cannot find enough now in summer, then what will become of us in the wintertime? We need the meat. We need the skins. My brother, Cameahwait, will go tomorrow. He has worked hard to learn to master the bow. He must prove himself to be ready to take my father's place as Chief someday."

"Look," interrupted Rabbit Ear. "Over yonder. In that sheltered spot by the stream. There are deer there. If we hurry, perhaps your brother could get here in time to shoot them before it is too dark." Sacajawea peered through the gathering twilight at the dark figures by the stream.

"They have come for a drink. They will not stay. I know their trail. I will try to turn them toward the camp. Go quickly and bring Cameahwait."

She slid down from her pony's back and dropped limply into the underbrush. If only the creatures would not be alarmed! If only she could reach the trail to turn them back in time! She moved silently. The sticks and stones had voices that would speak against her, she knew; but long ago she had learned to outwit them. She had often crept upon unsuspecting rabbits and birds, but this was the first time she had tried to creep up on so large an animal. Deer were clever and wary. She moved on silently, circling to windward of the two mother deer with their two sturdy fawns. Suddenly they left the stream and started up the trail that would lose them in the underbrush and darkness. She was almost on the trail when she heard their sharp hoofs clattering on the rocky trail that led from the stream. She called out and they paused and stood motionless. They sensed an enemy was near but did not seem to know on which side they were threatened. Then they broke into a run as if they knew their only safety was in the dense growth beyond. One fawn stopped and turned his head. Sacajawea realized suddenly that she held a stone in her hand and she hurled it with all her might. To her amazement the fawn dropped to the ground. Then she was upon him. He was only stunned and she knew she must end his life quickly. Excitement raced through her as she rose from her task. She had killed! There would be meat!

As she waited she made the bird call that was a signal between Rabbit Ear and herself. It would help them find her in the gathering darkness. Before they reached her she called to them, telling them the wonderful news.

"Meat. I killed it! I killed it!" Her voice rang with triumph. But her brother did not seem pleased. He had come with her friend thinking he might shoot the animal with an arrow and take it to camp in triumph, but to take in one that his sister had killed with a stone! They would laugh!

"I will take it," he said gruffly. "They shall believe I

19

killed it. Hold your tongue; remember, you know nothing."

"But I killed it," said Sacajawea, and then she remembered. It was important that Cameahwait should win the respect of their people. They must stop thinking of him as just a boy. If he brought this in to them now when they were hungry for food it would go far to win favor for him.

"Take it," she said. "We will follow slowly on foot and will speak no word. But remember! Save meat for us or our tongues may be loosened."

As they neared the camp they could hear the sounds of rejoicing. Everyone wanted a taste of the tender flesh, but one fawn, even a large one, could not satisfy them all. The girls found Cameahwait had kept his word, for there was a small portion for each of them—his own share, which he divided between them. Everyone was praising the young man. They planned a hunt on the morrow to follow the trail of the deer, and Cameahwait would lead them.

The camp was noisy and dusty. Children who should have been asleep whimpered and cried. But at last the wind swept away the warmth of the day and the warm skins felt good to Sacajawea on her bed on the hard ground. She decided not to go on the hunt with the squaws. There was an old squaw, the oldest member of the band, who might be able to tell her many things she wished to know.

It was not easy the next morning to get away from the small children who were left in camp, but at last she escaped them and found the old, old squaw sitting in a sheltered spot in the sun. Her tattered deerskin garment was no darker than her skin. Her face, wrinkled and puckered like a dried apple, was kept alive by her two small bright eyes that seemed to refuse to grow old.

"And you not upon the hunt?" asked the old woman in surprise as Sacajawea stretched out on the ground beside her. "I did not know you ever stayed behind with the old squaws and papooses."

"I wanted to talk with you. I am sure there is much that you can tell me that I would know. But tell me first why *you* did not go."

The wrinkled old face twisted into a wry smile. "Now I am old I am safer here. If danger overtakes the hunters the old and young may be left behind. I have known it to happen. You are young and could run and save yourself. No, no, I do not go unless the camp is moved. I like it here in the sun. It is food to me," and she nodded sleepily.

"Do not sleep now," begged Sacajawea. "I want to know where you have lived and what you have seen and done. Have you spent all your life on the western slope?"

"Oh no!" said the old one. "Once we lived on the plains beyond the eastern slope. Such a life—such a wonderful, wonderful life! Always so much food. Never any hunger. Meat, rich and juicy, from the buffalo. And such warm thick hides! Lots of warm robes and winter clothing and the finest moccasins."

"Tell me about it," begged Sacajawea. "What happened? Why did you leave this wonderful place?"

"We were once a great and a strong people. The Snake nation is like a great tree with many branches.

21

The Shoshone tribe is the western branch. Our people are Shoshones. Our land was plentiful in all the things we needed. Other tribes wanted our place. We had to fight to hold it. We had horses from friendly Indians to the south. We were strong and powerful. Our warriors rode out on their horses to meet any enemy. When they returned, it would be a night of dancing—a night of joy. They brought back treasures, scalp locks—sometimes of great leaders of other tribes—captured spears and weapons, and always captive prisoners. The warriors shared their hour of victory with us in the stories they told. As we listened we could almost see the frenzy of battle and hear the shouts of the victors and the screams of the dying. Our blood would boil with the same courage of the warriors which mounts so high that pain and danger seem to be forgotten."

She paused and seemed to be exhausted with the memory of those days, and then she added, "When I listened, sometimes I felt as if I had done the daring deeds."

She slept for a while and Sacajawea waited. When she wakened, Sacajawea asked her to tell more. "You have told me of the place where you lived, but tell me why you left it."

"Far to the east, to the land of the rising sun, there came strange people," said the old squaw wearily. "I have not seen them. I hope I never will. They bring misfortune. These people are said to have skins as white as milk, blue eyes and light-colored hair. Some of the medicine men say they are from the spirit world. I do not know. But they do have magic. Strange magic.

Smoking sticks that can kill at a great distance. Enemy tribes secured some of these deadly sticks and we were unable to defend ourselves against them. Our people were scattered. Some went one way and some another. We came across the mountains through the Lemhi Pass. Here we are safe from everything but hunger and cold."

Sacajawea nodded. These enemies she knew well. Sometimes they drove her people out on the eastern slope for food in spite of unfriendly tribes. "Do you know where the rivers run and where the birds go in winter?" she asked eagerly. The old woman shook her head. "I mean to find out," Sacajawea continued. "I want to know what lies beyond anything we know. Someday I am going to find out for myself."

A gleam came into the eyes of the old squaw as she said, "I wish we could be young together. Then I would go with you." They talked until she dropped to sleep. Sacajawea sat beside her until she heard the clatter of hoofs that told of the return of the hunters and she ran to join the others who rushed out to welcome them.

There was a great deal of excitement as the hunters came galloping home. And they brought meat!

There was enough for all. Food! Food! Food! They ate it greedily, hungrily, as though they never expected to taste food again. At least those who stayed at home ate greedily, for those who went on the hunt had already eaten their fill. What they brought back was what they could not consume. Hunters ate at once what they killed. Not to do so would be folly. An enemy might overtake them and take their food and leave them with their hunger. If that did not happen, then they carried home

23

what was left. And now everyone was happy. No one was hungry. They danced and sang for joy. Food, food, food, how wonderful it was!

Sacajawea ate hungrily. But as she ate she suddenly remembered the old, old squaw asleep in the sun. She had need for food, too, and the young Indian girl hurried to bring her to the feast before it was just a memory.

She found the old, old squaw still sleeping. She shook her gently and hurried her feastward while she was still in that borderland between waking and sleeping. When fully wakened with a piece of meat in her hand the old, old squaw turned her bright eyes to the young girl. Why was this child different, she wondered. Who would think or care about an old, old squaw? But the child's thoughtfulness warmed something within her.

There was a joyous time that night as they danced and sang and suddenly, in a lull in the rejoicing, there came to them the plaintive call of flying geese. Sacajawea slipped from the circle about the fire. Her mother put out her hand as if to hold her back, but she was gone. Another squaw turned to the mother and with a sneer on her face began to speak words that were quickly checked. She felt a hand on her arm. It was a thin hand, but strong, and the fingers bit into the flesh like teeth. She turned to face the old, old squaw.

"Hold your tongue," said the old, old squaw. "She feels what you shall never feel. She sees things to which your eyes are blind. Her eyes are as keen as a hawk's, and her ears as a she wolf's. She is not a clod."

The scornful one shrank back. She did not wish to clash with the "old one." No one seemed to notice when

Sacajawea slipped back into the circle. The squaws were busy talking together—and squatted near the small fire they had made was the old, old squaw, who looked up at her and smiled.

Chapter 2

The Hunt

The tribe had come into the Lemhi Valley early that spring and had drifted through the summer days idly doing what pleased them until they tired of it and turned to something else. Now that autumn was with them and the winter not far distant, Sacajawea began to think of the need for clothes and provision for the winter. Her older sister had become the wife of one of the braves of their tribe and no longer lived with them. Her father, the Chief, had sold her to him as was the custom of their people. The women of the tribe did all the work and the men looked after the hunting and fighting. Work was for squaws, not for warriors, and a man often had more than one squaw if he could afford it. Already, at twelve or thirteen years of age, Sacajawea was skilled in working with skins to make into clothing and was helpful with dressing and preparing meat for drying and making into pemmican.

All their clothing was made from animal skins—the dressed skins for summer clothing and the undressed for winter, with the fur worn on the inside. Pieces of bone were used for needles, and sinews or narrow strips of leather for lacing the garments together. She dreamed of the day when she would become so skillful that she could help make for her father, the Chief, the ceremonial garments so beautifully trimmed with fringes of fur, ermine tails, bears' claws, elks' teeth, polished horns, and other ornaments. Her clothes were very plain and a garment was worn until it was in rags before another was provided. Her long black hair was unkempt, for she thought no more of caring for it than the pony she rode cared about its mane. She liked it best when she rode against the wind and it fanned out behind her. Sometimes she bound it back with a narrow leather thong or a twisted strand of grass or wild flowers.

Life was simple in many ways. They had no need for dishes, for they ate with their hands. Cleanliness was not important to them. The struggle to provide enough food and clothing overshadowed everything else. Their problem was just to live.

Now the older ones were showing concern over their lack of preparation for the coming cold of winter, when they would have need for warmer clothing and food. There was so little time. The Chief called his leaders together. He told them they must have larger game. The small game that was available to them was not enough for their daily needs, so they must go out on the dreaded eastern slope and try to secure the buffalo that was to be found there. It was decided to send scouts to look over the land and bring back a report.

When the scouts returned they presented two plans. A short distance on the eastern side was a canyon, wide at the mouth but narrowing until its high steep walls met at the farther end, thus offering a trap for animals that might be driven within it. There was a herd grazing near by.

The second was farther away but offered a splendid opportunity. The herd was feeding near a deep gulch with high, straight sides. If it was possible to surround the herd on three sides and turn it toward the gulch, perhaps the animals could be driven over and in the rush many would be trampled and killed. It would be a rich harvest for the band. It would take little time, for in a few minutes the plan would prove to be a success or a failure. There would be no loss of arrows, so they could try the other plan if it failed.

There was much discussion among the hunters over which plan would be the best and the most successful. Cameahwait favored the blocked canyon. It was not so far away so it was safer for them, he reasoned. They could plant skilled marksmen on the canyon wall well before daylight. The herd was so near it would be as easy, he argued, to drive them into the canyon as it would be to drive them over the cliff. Either might fail, for buffaloes were stubborn animals and unpredictable.

But the idea of taking the animals so easily had its appeal to the band, even though it should bring them farther out in the enemy territory. It was decided to try the plan of driving the animals over the cliff.

"Cameahwait wants to show how skilled he is with the bow," said one of the braves. "He practices hours every day. You will have plenty of time to prove yourself, Cameahwait. The canyon wall is the easiest way. The scouts say there were no signs of our enemies."

"The easiest way is not always the best," said Cameahwait as he turned and left the gathering.

Of course they would not go upon a hunt or "to buffalo" without the usual festivities. They danced and sang and beat themselves into a frenzy of joy. The medicine men used all their knowledge to appease the evil spirits. When the merriment was at its height one of the men spoke to the Chief and they left together.

"I have a horse I want you to see," said the Indian. "The finest I have ever seen. You know horses, so your word will mean much to me."

It was tethered not far distant and the Chief knew when he laid his hand upon it that he, too, had never seen a finer animal. He loved horses and he had an overwhelming desire to possess it.

"He is young, Chief. I caught him upon the mountain-

29

side. I have broken him for riding and, although he is high-spirited, he is gentle and dependable."

"I will ride him," said the Chief eagerly, "and then I can tell you." He rode out into the darkness and was gone for a long time. When he returned he asked, "What do you want for him?"

"Your young squaw."

"I sold her several moons ago. A young buck gave me three ponies for her. Did you not know that?"

"I mean the little one."

"Sacajawea? She is a child."

"She does the work of a squaw. If I wait until she is older you will have promised her to someone else. If you wish this fine horse you may have him now and I will wait until after the hunt and the meat is cared for. Or I will wait for another winter if you wish. You know, Chief, that a good squaw is as scarce as a good horse."

"But I should have more than one horse," said the Chief.

"Not more than one horse like this."

The Chief sat in thought for some time. He loved horses. He wanted this beautiful animal. "It is agreed," he said slowly. "If I may have the horse now you may have the little squaw at some later time. But there is to be no word of it to anyone now."

"Your word is good to me, Chief. No word shall go from my mouth. I will tether this animal with your horses."

"I will ride it in the hunt tomorrow," said the Chief happily. "Such a fine animal, surely it will bring us good fortune!"

He had a strange uneasiness as he returned to the festivities. He did not like the man. In a way he had been tricked through his weakness for horseflesh. That the girl's mother would be angry to lose her best helper did not trouble him, for the wish of his squaw was of no importance. Cameahwait would not like it. He, too, did not like the man. There was a strange bond between Cameahwait and his sister that the Chief did not understand. Of course one was loyal to those of his own blanket, but still a man should remember that a squaw was a squaw.

He could hear the joyous sounds of his people and hurried to join them. There would be time, another winter, before anyone need know of his bargain. Before day they moved stealthily out on the eastern slope and traveled at night in order not to attract their enemies. At last they came near the place where three rivers joined to make the Missouri. Scouts brought word that the herd was still there at sunset, bedded down almost at the edge of the gulch.

Long before day the camp moved forward and, while the huge animals in the buffalo herd rested, the red men slipped silently in a semicircle about them. The great beasts roused at daybreak and rose sleepily from their grassy beds. The wind brought them no warning of the dangers that surrounded them. Near the edge of the gulch browsed three strange buffaloes. In mild curiosity the herd moved forward to greet them. Just as they neared the steepest side of the canyon wall the Indians rushed them. The three strange buffaloes turned into hideous, shouting, screaming savages! Hundreds of others sprang forth from clumps of bushes and the air was filled with a bedlam of bloodcurdling cries and shouts. The herd turned in terror for escape. Before them was the gulch, and down they ran. The rocks slipped beneath the feet of the leaders and they were pushed down by the frightened animals behind them. Slipping, tumbling, rolling, the herd swept down the steep side of the gulch, leaving behind those they had trampled in their escape.

The plan had worked! The Indians now plunged forward. Soon the squaws were skinning and cutting up the meat that would be life to them in the days that lay ahead. It was an hour of triumph! An hour of rejoicing at the success of their plan. But in their triumph they forgot to guard against that other enemy they always feared when on the eastern slope. While they had been surrounding the buffaloes, their enemies had been surrounding them!

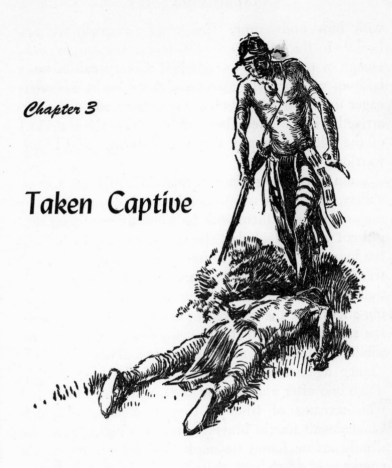

Chapter 3

Taken Captive

Sacajawea was one of the first to sound the alarm. She screamed the warning, the shrill tones of her voice telling the message to those who could not hear her words. Her people scattered, running for shelter or escape. They knew they were unprepared for battle and many of the men were unarmed, for they had come to drive the animals over the cliff rather than hunt them with bow and arrow. The Chief, Cameahwait, and leaders in the tribe tried to make a stand to cover the escape of the rest of the band. It was a small advance body of warriors who attacked—young bucks who were eager to take trophies before the larger body of fighters arrived. They wanted above all to possess the scalp lock of the Chief, a trophy that would bring fame to any warrior.

From her hiding place Sacajawea could see the invaders. Bare to the waist, their bodies hideously painted, they came upon them with bloodcurdling screams. She did not wish to look; but she could not help herself, for the horror of it seemed to freeze her as she watched. It was like something she had heard about; not something that could be really true. Their attackers had the smoking sticks that the old, old squaw had told her about— the smoking sticks that had made her people move for shelter behind the mountain range. They had little chance against them. She watched the enemy strike down one after another and then, when her father fell, with screams of triumph they took his scalp lock! Cameahwait fought bravely. From his hiding place his deadly arrow found its mark time after time, so the enemy paid dearly with their lives and with their horses. For a few moments it seemed as if they might triumph, but then they heard the reinforcements coming and knew that this was the moment they must escape. Cameahwait's horse had been shot down and his supply of arrows was diminished. Sacajawea saw him coming to her hiding place.

"Take my horse," she whispered. "Quick, you can

escape through the willows. They are not yet in sight."

He reached for the rein and disappeared in the thick growth. Sacajawea dared not move from her hiding place. She sat as if she were made of stone. She watched the enemy search out many members of her people from rocks and bushes. Men and boys were killed and old squaws and little children, but the strong squaws were taken prisoner. They would make good slaves. She hoped that they would pass her by. The slightest movement would attract their attention and would reveal her hiding place. If only they had listened to Cameahwait and had not come to this place! It was as he had said—"the easiest is not always the best." Cameahwait was wise and brave. If there were many who escaped he would no doubt be their leader, for he had proven himself.

Suddenly she heard a splashing in the water. A horse was moving up the little stream—a horse with an enemy rider upon his back. A great anger came to her and instinctively she reached out her hand to find a stone; but there were no stones, only a mossy bank! She realized too late that this sudden movement had been her undoing, as she looked up into a hideously painted face. The Indian was too quick for her and before she could crawl away under the low-hanging branches he had swung down and grabbed her by the arm. There was no use to fight; the whole world swirled about her. In an instant she would feel his knife. It was better to go quickly. But nothing happened. He drew her up on his horse before him and, bending under the branches, moved on upstream. She could hardly believe it. She had been spared. She had no desire to fight, for she had seen too much violence and death; so she did not resist and she made no outcry.

When night came Sacajawea found her friend, Rabbit Ear, among the many women and girls who had been taken prisoners. That night as she lay upon the ground with the stars overhead she remembered the joy they had all known the night before they started on the hunt. She told herself it was the last happy time she would ever know. There was no doubt in her mind what her fate would be. She would be a slave. She would work hard and there would be no time for dreaming. She tried not to hear the shouts and rejoicing of her captors. They were celebrating their victory and among their trophies the most cherished was the scalp lock of her chieftain father.

And so the next day and the next they trudged on and on, back to the camp of their conquerors. One night her friend, Rabbit Ear, told her that several of them planned to escape. They had been obedient and uncomplaining and the guard over them was relaxing. It would be fairly safe and anyway it was better than what lay ahead. "You will come with us," begged her friend.

Sacajawea did not answer for a long time and then she whispered, "Listen, do you not hear?"

"I hear nothing," Rabbit Ear answered.

But Sacajawea could hear the faraway plaintive notes of wild geese flying. They made her think of new places, faraway places. She could not go back. What was there to go back to? Work and hunger, a winter of starvation and cold. Unless her brother escaped, there would be no one of her blanket to welcome her. She had seen her father and mother killed and did not doubt her sister had shared their fate. No, she did not wish to go back. Life with the enemy would be hard work, too, but there were new hilltops each day. Perhaps this would be the fulfillment of her dream and would satisfy that longing she had always known. She must go on. She slept and dreamed that she heard the birds and answered them, saying that she was coming. When she awoke her friend was gone.

Chapter 4

The Camp of the Minataree

As the band of conquerors moved eastward they met another branch of their tribe. Among them were many squaws, into whose charge Sacajawea was given. There was work to be done and heavy burdens to be carried and she learned that if she worked willingly she could win a fair measure of favor from them. The load was heavy upon her young back; but she did not complain, and pressed on with an eagerness that they could not understand. For how could they know the urge within her? She bent beneath the load with hurrying feet as they drew near the crown of a hill, eager to see what lay beyond her vision. The next hilltop and the next and the next! What lay beyond them?

She always knew a thrill when she stood at last on a new point and drank in the view that lay ahead, putting it deep into her memory. She missed no small detail, little knowing that all this was an education for her—a training that was to make her valuable in the years to come.

The days went into weeks and they pushed on. Winter was near at hand, but to Sacajawea time meant nothing. She lived from the moment of waking to the instant she dropped asleep, erasing from her mind the memory of yesterday and refusing to think of tomorrow. But all things end. And at last they came to the camp of the Minatarees, also known as the Gros Ventres, near today's city of Bismarck, North Dakota. Only her eyes told of her interest in all she saw. Her face was stolid and expressionless, but her eyes missed nothing.

Her heart was beating fast. For the first time in her life she was to see how other people lived. These houses were not made of skin, nor were they shelters such as her people sometimes made from grass. They were made of earth and it was as if one stepped into a small hillside to enter them. Like a wild thing entering a place of danger she moved forward stealthily. Timidly she entered the doorway. The floor was about two feet below. Cautiously she stepped down. It was a huge room, about fifty feet in diameter. The floor under her feet was packed hard, almost like stone. In the center of the great circular room was a fire. It burned in a pit that had been dug about two feet below the level of the floor, and the edges of the pit were built up with stones. The light of the fire caught her eyes and held them and she followed the wisps of smoke that rose from it up through an opening in the domelike roof. And then she realized something else. There was a wonderful smell in the air. It made her hungry. Over the fire choice pieces of meat were slowly roasting, filling the room with a fragrance she had never known.

She breathed deeply. She was tired. Here was warmth and comfort. Here was protection from storms and hunger. Were these the things she sought and had she found them at last?

She hungrily ate her portion of roasted meat. It was good. She found her place to sleep under plenty of robes, and forgot to be afraid save when she dreamed again of other days that in her waking hours she shut out from her thoughts.

There was work to do, much work, always work, with the older women ever urging her to do more. Sacajawea was strong. It was not hard to work when she was not hungry. Although she was a prisoner she knew her life was no harder than that of the women of the tribe.

She liked the way the village was protected. It was built on a bend of the river, almost as if the river had put its arms around the city of mounds. On the open sides the Minatarees had built a high strong fence. On the inside of the fence they had dug a deep trench several feet deep. It made a fortresslike front that would hold back almost any enemy. All these things interested Sacajawea.

She had never dreamed of such security. Her people had always run before storms to sheltered spots. They were always fleeing from enemies, drifting from place to place with no protection.

When summer came again she worked in the fields. She had a hoe that was really the shoulder blade of the buffalo. With it she dug up the soil and planted the seed. Many other squaws worked with her. Nearly all of them had been taken prisoner and they were used as slave labor. It was very strange, Sacajawea thought, how they planted the seeds in the spring and tended them through the summer and at last harvested the corn, the beans, and the squash. Sacajawea knew many plants that grew wild whose roots had been food for her people, but these plants were strange to her. Her people did not plant and tend. All they did was to harvest. They harvested what nature planted and tended for them. They dug the roots and picked the berries. But they did not plant the seed or care for the growing plants.

No one noticed Sacajawea other than to see that she worked. Her thoughts she kept to herself. Many came to like her, for she was always a good and willing worker and they enjoyed the interest she showed in what they had and did. It made them feel important and superior.

They did not tell her that once they had been no better than the Lemhi band. They did not tell her that they had learned to make their houses and tend their crops from another tribe far superior to them. They did not tell her this, but she was soon to find it out for herself.

On the river not far from the Minatarees lived another Indian tribe, the Mandans. Sometimes they visited with the Minatarees and Sacajawea watched them curiously. They were different in appearance, for their skins were almost fair and many had blue or gray eyes. It was from these people that the Minatarees had learned their new ways. All this made Sacajawea wonder. If the Minatarees had learned from the Mandans, then from whom had the Mandans learned? There must be still something farther on! Farther on, perhaps beyond the next hilltop. And she would find out, someday!

By a stroke of good fortune she was allowed to help several squaws who were carrying supplies to barter with the Mandans. She was eager to see how they lived, and found dwellings the same type as that of the Minataree but of far better construction. She carried part of her load into one of these, a Mandan squaw leading the way. Although she showed no surprise her eyes missed no small detail. Instead of one great room it was divided off by buckskin curtains, making several rooms. Instead of sleeping on the floor there were built-up places on which robes were spread. And there were no drafts from the floor. The little girl from the Lemhi Valley had never dreamed of such luxury.

But in many ways the Mandans were no different from her own people. Here, too, the squaws did all the work. She did not wonder at that. The squaws always did the work.

She had heard of the white man. The old, old squaw had told her of him, but he seemed a sort of fable not nearly as real as the evil spirits she had always feared. She listened carefully for any news of the white man. He must be real and not too far away. These people spoke often of the "pale face." Sometimes one came to the camps to trade with them. He had much medicine, much good medicine. Sacajawea felt that the redskins, as she sometimes heard them call themselves, had a great deal of respect for the "pale face." As time passed, a trader or trapper from these strange people came their way. He was different, although his skin was sometimes tanned and weather-beaten almost to the shade of the red man's skin. But when he bared his arm it was white!

These men liked to talk with the Indians and usually were of a boastful nature. Through listening, Sacajawea came to feel that even the Mandans were of small importance and there was much they did not know. There was a great deal far beyond the hilltops. And as she relaxed her tired little body at night, waiting for sleep to come, she would hear that faraway whir of wings and the plaintive note of wild geese flying.

The first winter was long and cold. Much food had been stored away; but it was not sufficient, and there were times when everyone knew hunger. When the hunters brought back some small game everyone fought for his share. Sacajawea was slender and quick and she learned quite early that she must fight to live, and so she usually secured something for herself.

The springtime was the welcomed time. The river opened its gateway of ice and the birds returned. Again there was food for all. Sacajawea was even glad to work again under the hot sun with her crude bone hoe. But

when she rested, her eyes always sought the far horizons. Sometimes she felt trapped. How could she go on?
Could she go back to her people? The way was so long.
She thought back again over the miles, drawing out one
by one the pictures in her memory. At first there was so
much of interest in the new ways of the people with
whom she lived, but the old longing was returning to her
in greater force and the trapped bird of her desire
seemed to beat its wings in vain.

One day returning warriors brought back a new set
of prisoners and one of the squaws was put to work
beside Sacajawea. She came from the scattered tribe of
the Lemhi band and was able to give Sacajawea a little
knowledge of her people. Cameahwait, her brother, had
organized what was left of the tribe and they were living
in the Lemhi Valley as she had lived in that now so faraway day. But the new slave did not like the Minatarees,
nor the Mandans, nor the round earth houses, nor the
planted crops, and especially she hated the bone hoe.
She loathed and despised all of it and longed for the
day when she might find a way to return to her people.
She wanted to live again in the outdoors and in the skin
shelters. She wanted to run with the wind and be swept
by the storm into the sheltering valleys. She wanted
never, never to settle down in one place.

She said the Minatarees and the Mandans had taken
roots like the squash vines, and she spat upon the ground
to show her disgust. Let nature bring forth the plant and
she would dig it. As they worked day after day in the
hot sun Sacajawea came to understand many things.
Deep in her mind she had admired the houses and the

new way of living, but she was young and this woman was mature. She had hoped, without realizing it, that someday she could take some of these newfound ways back to her people in the Lemhi Valley. But it could never, never be. Her people would be like this squaw. They would hate it. They would never accept the safety and the shelter that it offered. They lived on danger and on fear as much as on food. The food was often gone, but the fear and danger were always with them. For them nature planted and raised the crop. They only plucked it when it was ready for the harvest.

The realization that her people would not accept a new form of life willingly, brought a change to Sacajawea. There was a barrier now between her and the Lemhi band, for she was no longer quite one of them; nor was she a Minataree, nor a Mandan. What had happened to her? What was she? She could not go back, and how could she go on?

Chapter 5

The Pale Face

One day a trader came to the camp. He was a Frenchman, bluff and boastful, but he was a white man. He talked of another world. To Sacajawea, squatting just beyond the light of the campfire before which he sat in the evening, chatting and bragging, his words were like new horizons. As she listened she felt as if she were standing on new hilltops! When the last sparks flickered, Sacajawea replenished the fire. From the first she had tried to learn the language of the Minatarees. She now had her reward, for otherwise she would not have been able to understand all the wonderful things the trapper had to relate. He had often visited the tribe and they were quite accustomed to him. He spoke Minataree well, but there was a strangeness about his speech that came from his native tongue.

All this had a fascination for Sacajawea. He was neither young nor attractive; he was not anything that she would have chosen for a master save that white blood flowed in his veins which made a link with another world that she longed to see. Perhaps he was like the Lemhi Pass in the mountain vastness through which she could enter and see the wonders of this other world.

Toussaint Charbonneau was a Frenchman, but he had spent so much of his life with the Indians that he was almost more of an Indian than the Indians themselves. He had learned that the Indian held the white man in high respect, so he had traded upon it when he came among them. The natives, at first curious, had now grown accustomed to him. His stories often failed to hold their interest, but he sensed that there was someone who listened, someone who drank in all he had to say, and so he polished his well-worn stories and added new luster to them. Perhaps he was a bit chagrined when he found that the listener was a child of thirteen or fourteen summers—a girl at that, captured from a far tribe who lived beyond the crest of the mountains in the Lemhi Valley.

He found it flattering, however, to have such an attentive listener. She was an intelligent girl, quick and always ready to do her part. He watched her work about the camp. He had one squaw, but she was stupid. She did her work as well as he could expect, but when she had time to rest she would fall asleep with no interest at all in his adventures. The more he thought about it the more he realized that the thing he needed was appreciation. He loved to talk and he loved to be listened to and, most of all, to be thought important. And so the girl slave came to be of value in his mind.

At last he decided to see if he could buy her. He went to the chieftain and asked what price he put upon the little slave. Slave squaws were plentiful. After every raid the warriors returned home with squaw prisoners who became slaves, so the price was not high. When Sacajawea was handed over to Charbonneau she may have been glad, for she had known the time would come when she would be sold and become some man's slave. It was the lot of every squaw whether with her own people or as a captive. But she had not dared to hope that her master would be a white man. What if he beat her? Probably any other would do the same. She could coax him to tell her what he had seen, and perhaps someday he might wish to go back to his people. The thought filled her with excitement. Walking behind him to his lodge, she heard a familiar sound. She stopped. She felt again the old call within her, but she made no sound. Charbonneau stopped too. He looked at her and then raised his face to the sky.

"By gar," he said, "the geese are flyin'."

It was not an easy life that Sacajawea came to know.

As the years crept by, more and heavier tasks were placed upon her. Otter Woman was her friend and showed no jealousy when Charbonneau decided that Sacajawea should be not only his slave but also his wife. Among the Indians a man often had many wives. The women did all the work and the men saved themselves for hunting and warfare.

The little flame that had always burned within her, even when danger or starvation threatened, now burned very low and at times threatened to flicker and go out. Charbonneau grew tired of telling his stories and seemed only to think of how heavy a task he could load upon her. He was surly and ugly and treated his squaws less kindly than his half-starved dogs.

Charbonneau was not a mountain pass that would lead her through the steep barriers into the land beyond the sunrise. No, he had no desire to return to the land of his people. He preferred the lazy life. He made the white man's life very wonderful in his stories. But there was something wrong. If it was so wonderful why was he content to be here, Sacajawea asked herself. It was all very puzzling. Her hopes drooped like a flower without water and she wondered why she had ever believed he would be the one to help her go on.

Without her dreams she would be another person. Without them she would become like Otter Woman, Charbonneau's other squaw. Otter Woman only wanted enough to eat and a fire to sit beside. Otter Woman had no dreams, but she did have a little son, Toussaint, named for his father. Perhaps he made her content.

Sacajawea looked at Otter Woman. Perhaps it was

better so. A squaw was just a slave. She did as she was told. It was the easiest thing to do—to let go and not care. But Sacajawea could not. This thing within her was the only thing that made life worth while, that made tomorrow worth living. If only the wild geese would fly again! If only once again she could hear their cry before the fire died within her, perhaps then she could rekindle it and warm herself by the flame of her dream. She tried to dream that she could hear the call, but it did not come to her.

In the days that followed, Sacajawea did not seem to care if her work was done or not. She did not care if Charbonneau raged and cuffed and kicked her. Otter Woman was puzzled. There was always much to be done and she was accustomed to have Sacajawea do part of her work as well. Charbonneau had traded for skins and they must work it into buckskin. But Sacajawea sat idle and listless.

They were then living near the Mandan village, for Charbonneau moved back and forth among the Indian people in order to keep a friendly standing with both tribes. Sacajawea had welcomed the change, for she had always longed to know more about the Mandans. She had learned to speak the Minataree tongue well and was learning some of the Mandan, but Charbonneau's scrambled French and English were still a mystery to her.

One day she decided to go for a walk, so she left her work and followed the river east of the village. It was nearly five summers since she had come from the home of her people as a captive slave. It had been many springtimes and harvests. Now she had seen seventeen summers. She had always the hope of going on. But now there seemed as little likelihood as there had been five years before.

It was as the woman of her tribe had said. She was like a squash vine and had taken root. Her people in the Lemhi Valley moved up into the north country, out on the eastern slope, up and down the streams wherever the call of nature with its fish, furs, and flesh directed them. Home was where they made their campfire. The thought set something singing within her. She would not be like the old, old squaw sitting in the sun. She was young and she would stay young and strong. Someday—and her eyes sought the far horizon, and for a moment she stood rooted to the spot! Were her eyes playing tricks on her? Could she believe what she saw? It was unbelievable. She rubbed her eyes and looked again. Moving majestically up the river was a huge boat with a sail. It was the largest she had ever seen. It moved slowly, for it was traveling upstream and men at the oars—many men— worked to move it. So fascinated was she with the great boat that it was sometime before she had much thought for the two smaller boats that followed it. It was as if the faraway other world was coming to her since she could not go to it.

But who could these people be? Were they another Indian tribe? Were they friend or enemy? She wasted no time in returning to the village. The boats were drawing near and the curious natives were thronging along the river to watch. Slowly, proudly the large craft followed by its two smaller companions made landing at the village and the men aboard them came clamoring out.

Sacajawea's eyes missed nothing. Here were white men, tall and straight. They seemed at ease, unafraid and even happy. She heard their voices, friendly and jolly. She wished that she could understand them. But perhaps Charbonneau could. And then she remembered the work she had left behind. She hurried to their lodge and went to work with such diligence that Otter Woman looked at her in amazement. What wonderful change had taken place? Sacajawea's fingers fairly flew and when at last Charbonneau swaggered in he was in high good humor.

The white men, his own people, had come! They had an abundance of supplies and equipment. They had a cannon, a huge "smoking stick," that gave forth sounds like cracks of thunder. He said the Indians could see now what great people the white men were. And they were friendly. He had talked with some of them. As Sacajawea listened to him some of the magic he told seemed to cling to him, for after all was he not a white man too? The fact that he was often cruel made no difference. The tribe was filled with curiosity and even Otter Woman slipped out to see and tried to bring back bits of information.

"There is a man with a skin black as night," reported Otter Woman. "Very big! Very strong! Hair like burnt grass, black and crinkly. Such white teeth when he laughs! His laugh is music like the river. Must come from faraway tribe. Much better than white man, much, much!"

The Indians seemed more interested in the black man than in any of the others, unless it was one of the leaders who had red hair. Sacajawea thought he was much more splendid than the black man. But it was all a great mystery. What were they doing here? Where were they going, or had they come to stay with the Mandans?

One day Charbonneau, being in a generous mood, explained to Sacajawea. It was not an easy thing to do, for there were so many things that Sacajawea did not know. But far to the east, he said, lived the white men, far toward the rising sun. They called their chief "President" instead of "Chief." The one they had now was named Jefferson. Jefferson wanted the land explored that lay between the Missouri River and the great water to the west. He had planned this great expedition. He had chosen two men, Captain Lewis and Captain Clark, to carry it out. They were in charge of everything—of the men, of the boats, and of all the supplies. The white men did not call themselves a tribe as did the Indians. This settlement of white men who had Jefferson for their chief or President, as they chose to call him, was known as the United States. It was a very odd name and Sacajawea wondered what it meant.

The expedition was costing a very great deal of money, Charbonneau said—all of twenty-five hundred dollars! The black man was the servant of Captain Clark. It had taken so long to come upstream against the current that they planned to spend the winter at the Mandan village and go on when the ice broke in the springtime. They were going to build a log fort in which to spend the winter.

All these stories were very fascinating to Sacajawea and she worked hard to win Charbonneau's approval so that he would tell her more. She knew that there was a meeting of the white men with the Mandan chiefs and she heard of the wonderful things they gave the Indians—beads, bells, shining bits of tinsel, and bits of glass in which you could see your face! She had seen her face in a calm pool of water, but this was so much more clear. It was wonderful and she hoped someday that she, too, might have one of these "looking glasses."

And now the sound of axes felling trees could be heard and the Indians gathered and looked on with wonder as the fort grew up log by log under the guidance of Patrick Gass, head carpenter. The white men kept close guard on their supplies, for they still had a long way to go before their mission was ended. It was going to be a much longer and harder trip than they had anticipated, for they had been unable to travel farther than fifteen miles a day against the strong river current. Soon they had stout quarters in which to store their food supplies and ammunition. The ammunition was stored in canisters that could be melted and run into bullets. There were many bales of supplies and these were divided so that if one bale was lost the entire supply of one item would not be lost to them. As soon as all was safe in storage the hunters went forth for game, to lay in a supply of food against the coming winter months. They prepared jerked meat after the Indian fashion and worked the pelts and skins into leather for clothing. Such industry the red man had never known.

Chapter 6

The Coming of Lewis and Clark

One day Charbonneau came home in a particularly good mood. He had learned that the white men needed guides and he had offered his services.

"Take me," begged Sacajawea.

"You are a squaw," he answered. "White men do not want squaws. They leave their own squaws at home. I will be a guide and interpreter."

"But let me go," begged Sacajawea. "I will carry your load. I will gather roots and food. I will tend your fire." She was almost on her knees begging.

"Go back to your work," he said roughly. "There is much to do. We need much buckskin and moccasins and clothing made. Always you want to talk, talk, talk. Get to work."

But Charbonneau was not too sure of being chosen to go with the expedition. He knew he had little respect in the eyes of the two Captains, Lewis and Clark. They showed little interest in the swaggering Frenchman until they discovered one of his squaws came from across the mountains and was a Shoshone. The Shoshone tribe was an offshoot of the great Snake Indian tribe, but due to misfortunes they had been scattered and now wandered in many small bands as did Sacajawea's people. No expedition of white men had ever gone beyond their territory. They were feared by the white men, for they held a place in the mountain vastness that no white man had ever passed. They knew the valleys and the cliffs and the canyons and the white man did not, so he would be at their mercy when he entered their territory.

The Captains, Lewis and Clark, were busy piecing together the bits of information they were able to gather. They questioned Charbonneau with care. He assured them that his young squaw was of this feared tribe. She had been captured when she was quite young, but she remembered well the journey across the hundreds of miles that lay between the Mandan village and the Lemhi Valley. He also assured them she remembered well her native tongue.

Together the two Captains argued. "No Indian squaw would be intelligent enough to help us on our mission," said Lewis. "I cannot believe all the things this man says. We know his kind. Only a lazy and shiftless man would be willing to come and spend his life with the Indians. He would tell us anything to get his way."

"But he says she is different from other squaws," said Clark. "That could be. I was amused at his claim that all credit was due to him, that he had trained her and made her alert and intelligent. At least, Captain Lewis, there is a possibility that some of this may be true. If she could speak the language and give us any friendly contact with those mountain tribes her value would be without price. If she is of any value to us it will be purely providential. But such things do happen. Even I believe that miracles happen all around us."

"It will be a miracle indeed," said Lewis. "But it's worth taking the chance. She will be little burden to the expedition and no doubt we can use the Frenchman. He has lived with Indians and knows their ways. Have him bring the squaw over and we will question her. We may find something to reassure us. These Mandans have always been friendly with the whites, but I confess that I break into a sweat, even in my dreams, when I think of meeting that roving band who have come to believe that every stranger is an enemy. Tell the Frenchman to bring his squaw here. Perhaps we can judge better if we see her."

Charbonneau was angry when he returned to his lodge that evening. He almost decided to give up all idea of joining the expedition. If they took him only because of his squaw, it would hurt his vanity. On the other hand, he could go and take his squaws. Sacajawea need never know that she was of any value, for he was the only one who could talk with her. He commanded his squaws to make ready to go with him. Otter Woman grunted unhappily. She would rather sit by the fire. He was in a bad mood, a very bad one, she thought. So there was nothing to do but go with him as cheerfully as possible, for he could be very unpleasant. They set out, Charbonneau in the lead and the Indian squaws following in single file.

When they reached the fort they were invited in. Even Otter Woman was interested now. The Indians were always curious and it was not often the lot of any of them to enter the stout log building. Charbonneau waved them to one side and the two squaws squatted together against the outer wall while he went to talk with the white chiefs. Sacajawea's quick eyes missed nothing and in her heart she felt a strange excitement. What could be the meaning of their coming here? Had he at last decided to go with the expedition? She dared not think of it, for it was too wonderful to be true.

She watched the men talking together and noticed the white men were looking at her and Otter Woman. Then to her surprise Charbonneau turned and beckoned her to join him as he talked with Captains Lewis and Clark. She wished she could understand all they said, but her only contact was through Charbonneau. He could speak the Minataree language and translate to her in this tongue what the white man wished to say.

"They want to ask you some things," said Charbonneau. "They will ask me and I will ask you and then tell them what you say. They want to know about your people and where they live."

"They live across the mountains," said Sacajawea. "Far away. They were driven back from the eastern slope by fierce Indian tribes who had the white man's smoking sticks. Now they find shelter in the mountain canyons and valleys and are safe."

"Would you know the way back?"

Know the way back! She remembered every hilltop. The white men who watched knew her answer even though they could not speak her language. The way back was like a book that she had read and memorized every page. Did she know the way back! The white Captains turned to each other and smiled. It looked good, very good. The little squaw would never put on an act like that. She would know.

But it had been a long time since she had left her people. She now had learned a new language. What of the old one? Could she still speak it or would it be dimmed by the passing years in her memory? Could she still speak it and did she think that she would know her people after many years of separation?

That was too much! Know her native tongue? Know her people? The words that fell from her lips were strange to Charbonneau. She burst forth in a flood of Shoshone like a stream that had long been dammed up and held back.

"Speak in Minataree," he said gruffly. "Keep that until we reach that mountain tribe of yours."

For a moment no word was spoken. But the white

men watching saw that within the young body of the slender squaw was a spirit that would not be broken by her overbearing master. For a moment she looked at him and there was no cringing. Then his words seemed to come to her. "Until we reach that mountain tribe of yours." That must mean that he was going to take her with him! And suddenly her eyes smiled. She remembered. She could speak the tongue. She would know her people. Why, they were of the same blanket! Her brother, Cameahwait, if living, would be their leader. There was her sister, too, for one of the Shoshone slaves had told her she survived the massacre. She knew them all. They would be glad to see her again.

Would her people have horses? Horses would be needed to cross the mountains to the river. They would be well paid for them. Sacajawea nodded. Surely she could prevail upon her people for this help.

As she stood before them still wrapped in her robe of buffalo skins they noted her proud and graceful bearing. She was small in stature with soft brown skin and good features. It was her eyes that held them. Her eyes talked to them. They seemed to illumine her whole face as she spoke of her home. She was alert and intelligent, there was no doubt. They looked at her and then at the swaggering Frenchman and felt a great pity for her.

Lewis and Clark watched with interest and nodded together. It seemed a marvelous piece of good fortune that they should find this member of the feared mountain tribe here and in the hands of an interpreter. She was different. Each man told himself that he must not expect too much, for after all she was just an Indian squaw and what seemed to be so good now might vanish by tomorrow. They looked at Otter Woman. They could never take anyone like Otter Woman.

"We'll take you with us," they told Charbonneau, "you and the young squaw. As soon as the river opens in the spring we'll start, so that is settled. And take good care of the squaw," they warned, "for we take both of you or neither one."

Chapter 7

Little Pomp

The following day they again sent for Charbonneau and his young squaw.

"Do the Indians have any marriage ceremony?" asked Captain Lewis. "Are you married to her?"

Charbonneau smiled. The Captains were surely very ignorant.

"I bought her," he told them. "Squaws are slaves. They belong to a man when he buys them. He can do what he will with them and he can have as many as he can afford to buy. If one runs away he can follow her and beat her to death if he wishes. It is enough to give a horse for a squaw. That is all the ceremony there is. This is not the white man's land nor is it ruled by white man's ways."

"We are not trying to rule the land," said Captain Clark, "but we expect to rule the expedition. We can understand that these Indians know no better way, but you do. We have decided that before you go with us you must be married to this squaw with the white man's ceremony. I know," he hastened as Charbonneau started to complain, "I know she will not understand it, but you will and all of us in the expedition will know that she is truly your wife according to the white man's laws. If you wish to go with us, acquaint her with what we are about to do."

Charbonneau talked with Sacajawea. He could tell her what he wished, for the Captains would not understand. So he told her that the white man had a ceremony, that he read something from a book when his people married. He thought, "The Captains will hear me say 'married' to her, but she does not know what it means."

"Married?" she repeated. "What does it mean?"

"It means you become my squaw. It is silly. I bought you from the Chief; but they wish to read to us, so do as you are told." She nodded.

Captain Clark read them the ceremony line by line from a book, pausing for Charbonneau to explain it to his little squaw.

"It is a promise," said Charbonneau. "That is all. You promise and I promise." So they were married. The

Captains sighed as they watched them go back to their lodge.

"A strange wedding," said Captain Lewis. "It means nothing to them."

"But it does mean something to us and it will to the men," answered Captain Clark. "The time will come when her people will choose this way. It will take a long time, but perhaps when she is very, very old she may remember that she was the first one of her people to be married by the white man's ceremony."

"To such a scallywag," said Captain Lewis, "how can it be a happy memory?"

Winter closed the river with ice and the snow lay deep upon the ground when word came one day inviting Charbonneau and his young squaw to the fort to help celebrate Christmas Day. Christmas, what was Christmas, Sacajawea wondered and she was filled with curiosity. They found the camp in a merry mood and the Captains gave each of them a small gift and a greeting.

She heard it over and over. "Merry Christmas, Merry Christmas." All the men were jolly. They laughed together and one of them, Cruzatte, played his violin.

The violin was very wonderful to Sacajawea. It was almost like a thing alive. Sometimes it seemed to sob and cry and then it would raise its voice high as if in triumph. It would dance, never touching its feet to the ground, and float away like a cloud. She watched it in the hands of the white man whose fingers flew over its strings as he held it closely between his head and shoulder. Perhaps he breathed some of the song into it. The men called for merry music, for music that made the feet tap. They wanted to be gay. They wanted the music to laugh with them and every man did his best to make the evening a festive one. Many of them had memories of other Christmas days and of loved ones hundreds of miles away, and only by doing all they could to make it a happy day for the others could they forget and find happiness for themselves. Sacajawea was puzzled. Her people danced before a hunt. They danced before going to war. They danced when they wanted something very much. By dancing they seemed to beat themselves into a high pitch of confidence that helped them succeed in doing the thing they were about to attempt. But why did the white man dance? Was he about to go on a great hunt or into battle? She asked Charbonneau, for he was in a good mood and her questions seemed to amuse rather than irritate him as they so often did. He wanted to tell her, but he found it difficult to explain. There was no one else to do it, so for once he made an honest effort.

"The white man," he explained haltingly, "believes in someone he calls God. His God made the world and the sun and the stars and the moon and everything. He made the people and he wanted them to be good. But the people were bad, many of them very bad." He paused. What could God mean to her, he wondered. And how could he tell her of the angels? To her the spirit world was a world of fear. So he said, "Christmas is the birthday of a baby born in a manger in a stable, long, long ago. And a star came and stood over the stable where the young child lay."

"What is a stable?" asked Sacajawea.

"A shelter for the animals to keep out of the storm. God's son was born in a manger. And a star, a bright star, came and stood over the manger. Out on the hillside a shepherd watched his sheep and he saw the star. Other shepherds, watching, saw it. They came to the manger and saw the baby. They worshiped him. He was named Jesus. Today, this day, is his birthday. They call it Christmas. Where the white man lives, all over the world this is Christmas. There is gladness." He sighed. "I had almost forgotten; it all seems so long ago since I kept Christmas."

"Was it long ago that he lived?" asked Sacajawea.

"Long, long ago—many, many old men," he answered. She had no idea of numbers; this was the only way he could tell her.

"But how do the white men know all this?"

"It is written," answered Charbonneau.

"Where?" Sacajawea wanted to know more about the white man's ways. "Is it written somewhere on the rocks? Could I see it someday?"

He sighed. There was so much she did not know, but he did his best. "You have seen the Captains making marks on what they call paper." She nodded. "That is writing. White men write down on paper the words they have in their mouths. Then it is not forgotten. Many pieces of paper fastened together make a book. Hundreds of years ago when the baby was born many people wrote it down and these writings were kept. So it is not just one man that says it is so. It is many. And as the baby grew and did many wonderful things, these were written too. It is all in a book. It is the Bible."

He said the word reverently. How strange that he remembered these things! How many years had it been since he had thought of them?

She was silent for a few minutes and then she said, as if she were talking to herself, "Then they are not dancing to drive away devils and evil spirits but because a long time ago a little baby was born."

Charbonneau nodded.

"White man has strange medicine," she whispered, "but it is good. Very good." She was satisfied and asked no more, but she sat thinking. The music soothed her and something within her knew a strange new joy; for it was Christmas Day, the birthday of God's son born in a stable with a star standing guard overhead. There was much she did not understand, but she did understand about babies and stars. And she thought to herself, "Will a star stand overhead when my child is born?"

In February Sacajawea's son was born. The day was cold, but she lay under the warm buffalo robes with her baby nestled close. She was very weak and tired, but she called Charbonneau to her side and whispered, "Charbonneau, will you do something for me?" There was such pleading wistfulness in her voice and eyes that he nodded.

"Then look out and see if there is a star," she whispered. She saw the look of bewilderment on his face and then he turned. If it would please her he could look. Probably some stupid superstition of her people. He took his time about looking but returned at last.

"Did you see one?" she asked breathlessly.

He nodded. "A whole sky full of them," he answered, and watched a look of contentment steal across her face as she closed her eyes and slept.

Every member of the Lewis and Clark Expedition found interest in the new member of their group. Captains Lewis and Clark developed a watchful and protective interest. Captain Lewis had a fair knowledge of medicine and he made use of all he knew to make the young Indian mother well and strong. Captain Clark, who was quite as interested, made it his duty to see that she received good treatment from those about her. Charbonneau, who suddenly found his child of interest to the white men, gained a measure of pride in it himself. They named the boy Baptiste, an old-time French name that Charbonneau knew and liked. But Sacajawea called her son "Pomp," for in her native tongue it meant "first-born."

One day at the fort a group of men sat idly together. Two of them were playing a game of mumble-de-peg with their knives while other watched and chatted.

"I can't see why the Captains are so bound and determined to take along that squaw," said one. "Now she has a papoose, I should think that would settle it."

"Can't see either," agreed another. "If we had wanted any women along we could have brought our own. But we left them where they belong, safe, back home, and that is where she should be too. Idea of traipsing over the country with an Indian woman in the party!"

"Listen," said York, the huge Negro who was Captain Clark's servant. "Now look at this," and he drew from his pocket a rabbit's foot. "Now I wouldn't relish going anywhere without this. A lot of you think it silly. Call it superstitious. When I have it here in my pocket it makes me feel safe, and sometimes I put my hand in my pocket just to feel it and know it's there when things get ticklish. The day we came up the river and all those savages crowded us, as sure as I'm from Kentucky, my scalp began to creep and I began to have funny feelings running through me. But I just put my hand on this little old rabbit foot and they all took off. I felt just as brave as a lion!"

"What does that have to do with a squaw?" asked a querulous voice.

"Just you listen and I'll tell you. She's going to keep away the danger. If anything would happen to her now, I wonder if we would be a-going on."

"Shucks, that's silly talk, York," said one of the players as he made a careful balance of his knife before tossing it in the game. "Silly to think a gang of men like us, tough and used to hardships, would be helped or stopped by a squaw."

York nodded. "Sure sounds that way, boss. But what can this little old rabbit's foot do, and me a big strong man? The squaw is going to keep away the evil just because she is along."

"Well, don't tell that to Captain Clark or he'd skin you alive," said another. "I don't know anyone that has the brains and courage of our Captain Clark. If anyone can be a rabbit foot, then he's mine. When he's in the party, then I'm not scared."

"That's the way I feel too," joined in another. "And if the Captain thinks there is good in taking the little squaw, I'm for taking her. But I don't like that husband of hers. He's low-down and mean and dirty. That fellow would sell out on you if you got into a tight pinch. We don't need too many of his kind with us, but the only way we can talk to the squaw is through him. I guess you'd call him a necessary evil."

"It makes a heap of sense to take her," a new voice broke in, "if she can give us one bit of help with those redskins we're going to meet out yonder. They're her own kinfolk. She may save all our scalps; and I'm for treating her like a white woman, and heaven help any of you who don't. Have to keep her friendly to us or she won't do us a mite of good."

"Ought to be mighty thankful she's the kind of squaw she is," said another. "If she were one of those big clods it would weight us down carrying her upstream. If her people are like her they'll make one of two things, good friends or bad enemies. You'll see. And don't forget this—her people have to be more than friendly; they have to be helpful too. The Captains are not talking about it, but we will need horses and they have them. We know this from the Minatarees, for they are sort of second cousins to the Pahkees who made all the trouble out there for our little squaw's people. When we go over the mountain pass the streams will be too small or too swift for boats and we'll need horses."

Sacajawea was unaware that she was the subject of so much speculation, but she did know that the white men were interested in her and her child. Although she could not speak their language she watched their faces. They spoke so gently, almost in whispers, when they came to see the baby, and tiptoed in and out. One day when the redheaded Captain Clark held out his finger and the baby hand clutched it, they all laughed together. She could not know what they said; but she understood their tones and their meaning, for kindness needs no interpreter. In her eagerness she tried to tell them that she would make them no trouble, for Pomp upon her back would be as light as a feather, and that she would do her share and more if they would take her and her child.

The gift they brought her, she thought, was the most beautiful thing she had ever seen, except, of course, her baby. It was a belt of blue beads.

Chapter 8

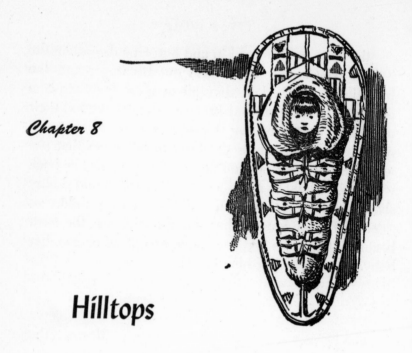

Hilltops

The winter seemed endless to those who waited for the springtime. But at last the ice began to break and high in the sky flew the wild geese, again returning to their summer homes. Sacajawea no longer ran calling to them as she did when she was a child. But their cries aroused the same strange urge within her that they had in that faraway day. Now that she was to leave the place where she had lived so long, she felt a strange singing within her. Once more she would break the bonds that held her. The roots, were they? The squash vines? And there would be hilltops—another, and another, and yet another, on and on and on!

72

It was in April, 1805, that they started at last, setting out in two large pirogues and six canoes. The natives swarmed the river banks watching them make ready to set out. Sacajawea felt very proud in her new fringed buckskin dress with its beautiful blue bead belt. Her moccasins were new too. They were made with leggings attached to form high boots. Charbonneau had demanded new clothing for them both, and she and Otter Woman had worked many days to make it. Upon her back hung a "papoose board" with her papoose, Baptiste, snugly cradled within it. It was the most beautiful board she had ever seen, for it was made of the finest material and workmanship. The board was padded and covered with soft leather, and the leather pouch attached to it was perfectly shaped to hold the little body. It was fringed for added beauty, as was the tiny headpiece that slipped over the baby's head like a cap. A wide band of leather was attached to the board to hold it firmly over her shoulders so she could carry her baby with ease upon her back.

Her hair was neatly parted in the middle, drawn forward to form two heavy black braids that framed her face and hung before her where they were out of the way of the board, and perhaps, too, out of reach of baby hands. She had learned to wear her hair in this way from the Mandans, who had many habits of neatness that her people had not yet learned.

She told Otter Woman and her little son, Toussaint, good-by, for they were to stay at the Mandan village. Now she stood ready to go, and filled with eagerness.

Everyone was in his place. Everyone was happy. At

last, at last they were on their way. This was the day for which the white men had yearned. It did not matter how hard the way would be if they could only be at it. The hardest thing was waiting, and thinking of what lay ahead. Now, at last, they were off.

They fought the river. Day after day from early dawn till dark they fought the river. It was as if it held out its watery hands and pushed them back, but they would not be held back. They bent to their oars with even more determination. It was hard moving upstream with such heavily loaded crafts, but they had no choice. The way was long and they needed a plentiful supply of food, clothing, and ammunition for themselves, and gifts for the Indians they would meet upon the way.

They fought the wind. The wind might have been their friend had it blown from the east rather than the west, but it seemed to have joined forces with the river as if it, too, said, "Keep back; this is not for you." With unseen hands it held them back, but it could not stop them.

There were many pitfalls that nature seemed to plan to hold this land for itself and its native people. Sometimes the river bed grew wide and shallow and the oars caught in the sand and gravel. Instead of being stopped the white men fastened ropes on the boats while men on the shore tugged and pulled the loaded crafts up the shallow stream. The progress was slow, but they moved on! Just when they had triumphed over one difficulty another rose to meet them, but nothing could stop them.

Sacajawea did her part, although behind that mask of unexpressiveness that was ever on her face she gave no sign of her thoughts. No one guessed that she compared the white men to her people. When her people found fishing hard they left it and went hunting. The camp on the Knife River took root in its safety. But the white men did not stop when things were hard; they triumphed over them. Nor did they stop in safety; they pressed on. It was all very strange that the white men and the red men were so different.

In one way nature was kind. There was an abundance of game, and when someone grumbled he was often told that at least he did not have to work on an empty stomach. The hunters in the party kept them well supplied with meat in a great variety, for there were buffalo, antelope, and deer as well as geese, ducks, and prairie chickens. They were always amused at the eagerness with which the young Indian mother, at every stopping place, went forth to dig roots, long known to the Indian as good food. It was amazing the way she could tell the good roots from the bad, and the quickness and skill with which she gathered them. The men who tasted them found them good and they liked the added variety to their rather limited diet. The men came to depend upon her for this and she felt she was having a part in the adventure.

At night, as dusk gathered, they beached their boats and everyone went to work to make the camp. They made a fire with whatever was at hand. Sometimes the wood was green or wet and there was more smoke than heat, but they were clever and made the most of what was to be had. After they had eaten and the camp was ready to settle down for the night, Captain Clark liked to

75

have Sacajawea teach him a few simple words of her language to prepare him for the day when he would meet her people.

She would sit before the flickering firelight with her baby sleeping on her lap. Her round girlish face framed by her long, black braids would become animated in her eagerness to express herself. At times her fingers flew to tell in sign language what her tongue could not. Charbonneau would be the interpreter. And she learned too. Bit by bit she learned the words of French and English. These were proud moments for the little Indian mother and she came to look forward to them.

The days became warmer as the weeks passed, although in the stillness of night the cold crept back under the cover of darkness as if reluctant to yield to springtime's warmth. Sacajawea was used to the life. She had known cold and all its cunning from earliest childhood. There had been no softness in life for her. The hard ground was a good bed and hard work had always been her lot. Often when a man was about to grumble over a task he looked at her, so eager to do her part, with her child strapped upon her back, and held back the words. In watching her the men gained strength for themselves.

In turn, she watched them. She pondered over many things. Her people would have taken their women to do the work, to make the camps, to lift and carry the load. But where were the white men's women? She heard talk of wives, mothers, and sisters safe at home in the white men's camp—and the white men did women's work! Although she stepped forward always to do her part, these men grumbled when she tried to carry a load or do a heavy task. They would take it from her and mutter words that she could not understand, but their gestures told her that they thought she did enough with the baby on her back.

Sometimes she would see that Charbonneau noticed it, too, and there would be a black look in his eyes. No doubt he was thinking that they were spoiling her, treating her like a white woman when she was just an Indian squaw.

But Sacajawea was taking one day at a time. She always watched for signs, for she understood that they depended upon her to read Mother Nature's book and tell them all she learned from it. She was glad that they felt she was a good reader and trusted her. And so she sharpened every instinct within her to see and understand all that could be seen and understood.

She told them of tracks of animals and how old they might be. She recognized trails of other Indians and old camps. Some were new, some old. She warned them of bad water, and of plants and roots that were good or poisonous. Bit by bit they came to lean upon her for this information and she was thrilled at having a part in something the white men thought to be important.

But the more valuable she became to the white men the more surly Charbonneau became. He was the one upon whom they should depend, he thought. He should be more important. His squaw was being treated with more respect than he, Charbonneau, French trapper, hunter, trader, and interpreter. Captain Clark was aware of this. He knew that the man was not to be trusted and he was anxious about the girl's safety. He gave the

Frenchman many grave warnings and several of the men told Charbonneau what his fate would be if he harmed his young Indian squaw. He was too far away now to dare to do anything drastic. He was not in a friendly land and he had no doubt the white man would keep his word if he harmed her. Whenever it was possible to give Sacajawea a blow or a kick without the white man's knowledge, he did not fail to do so; for in his jealous heart he knew that she was faithful to him and would not reveal his cruelty. Kicks and cruel treatment were not unknown to Sacajawea and she accepted them as she did the other hardships of life.

Chapter 9

A Daring Rescue

Sacajawea warned of great bears as they moved on their westward journey. She told of their fierceness and how dangerous they were. These great bears would fight even when filled with arrows. But the men were unbelieving. All her information had to come through Charbonneau, for no one could speak Minataree but the Frenchman. Knowing how unreliable he was, they often "took a pinch of salt" with the stories he told and the information he claimed the young Indian squaw gave them.

"Couldn't tell the truth if he was to be hung for it," said one. "Probably are big bears, but not that big. Anyway we aren't worried."

They often teased one of the men, Bratton, who preferred walking along the river bank to riding in the boats. "Better watch out for bears, Bratton. They're big out here. Take you down like a pill without even putting a nick in you, I'll wager."

But one day they were surprised to see Bratton running along the bank, calling for help. He had encountered one of the bears. A bear such as the Indian girl had told about. Big? It was a monster! He had wounded it, but the dumb thing didn't know enough to be wounded. It just kept coming. Bratton, with his musket empty and no time for reloading, had beat a hasty retreat with the bear at his heels. There was great excitement among the men and a party was organized to find this monster of the wilderness. There were many skilled hunters who looked forward to just such an adventure. They found the animal and it proved to be as big as Bratton had said and made the Indian girl's warning a true one. To most of the men this made the trip far more interesting. They wanted adventure. And here it was, a bear with a footprint twelve inches long and seven inches wide. Everyone was on the alert for more bears. It was the talk of the campfires and every man hoped to be the first to see the next one. But the days passed and the bears seemed to have sensed the white man's coming. "Guess they all took to the woods," said one of the men. "Guess they don't relish the smell of gunpowder. I'd give a pewter dollar to get a shot at one of the brutes."

One day he got his wish; for as the boats moved slowly up the river, there, lying upon a huge flat rock sunning himself, was a tremendous bear.

Drewyer, who was an expert shot, was steering the pirogue. He turned to find someone to take his place, for he wanted more than anything else in the world to be the one to bring down the great beast. The only one at hand was the Frenchman, Charbonneau, who preferred to stay in the boat. Taking a canoe and four companions, Drewyer set out after the huge beast. He had an exciting time, but not as exciting or more dangerous than did the occupants of the pirogue with Charbonneau in charge.

Being given a job of importance was like a stimulant to the Frenchman. He began bragging and boasting of his hunting and trapping days. His stories were colorful, but he could not tell them without the use of his hands.

"Keep your hands on that rudder and pay attention to what you do," called one of the men in the pirogue. "Drewyer must be crazy to put you there."

But the warning was too late. The wind had caught the white man napping. With almost malicious glee it swept the craft about and out of control, filling it with water. Charbonneau, unable to swim, forgot his story and began to cry and pray. Cruzatte, who was at the oars, shouted, "Get hold of that rudder."

As the pirogue filled with water, instruments and irreplaceable and valuable papers belonging to the Captains, and other bits of equipment, began to float out into the stream. Bedlam reigned. Charbonneau was completely helpless from fright. The men at the oars screamed at him to do something to save the valuable articles. But Sacajawea, who, some of them said, wanted only a place to sleep and plenty to eat, saw and understood. With her child on her back she plunged into the icy stream and swam out to the floating things as they moved into the current. She knew they were valued by the Captains. The expedition could go on without Charbonneau or Cruzatte, perhaps even without the pirogue, but the compass and the instruments were necessary.

Nothing was lost. The tricky waters could not whip the valuable things past her reach. She was so intent on her task that she did not hear Cruzatte threaten to shoot Charbonneau if he did not come to his senses and right the craft. Charbonneau had little doubt Cruzatte would shoot, and that was worse than drowning. Soon they were bailing out the water and helping Sacajawea into the boat and preparing to make a landing where they might dry out.

There was much excitement that night recounting the adventures of the day, for the men who had gone on the bear hunt had returned with more respect for a bear than they had ever expected to admit. Six men had gone out for the bear, who had, at first sight, seemed to be taking a sun bath on a rock. The bear had little respect for bullets, and four of the men were almost attacked when Colter, who was a skilled hunter, shot and killed the animal.

Peter Cruzatte told in detail about the afternoon upset of the pirogue.

"It's a good thing there was one person who kept his head or, rather, her head," said Captain Clark dryly. "But for Janey, here"—and he turned to Sacajawea, whom he often called Janey—"we might all be wondering if we would dare to go on. I'd not like to try it without the instruments that she saved for us today. I don't know," he added, almost as if to himself, "how she knew they were valuable. She keeps so quiet, and our only contact is through that renegade husband of hers. An Indian girl, a wild young thing, almost like a deer, how could she know, how could she think to save them for us?"

Then Captain Lewis called Charbonneau and the little squaw. "Tell her," he instructed the Frenchman, "tell her of our gratitude to her for saving our equipment this day. It was a brave deed and a dangerous one. We are grateful. And give her this." He held out a string of beads that he had taken from their pack. "Tell her when she wears it she will remember that she did something of real value to the expedition."

He did not know what Charbonneau told her, for he did not know the language of the Minataree; but he could tell from the look of joy on the face of the little squaw that she was pleased. She held the beads in the light of the fire and delighted in them.

That night Captain Lewis wrote in his diary: "The Indian woman, to whom I ascribe equal fortitude and resolution with any person on board at the time of the accident, caught and preserved most of the light articles that were washed overboard."

That night they named a creek Sacajawea Creek!

The path they followed was not the one that had brought Sacajawea to the camp of the Minataree on the Knife River. The broad highway of the Missouri was familiar for some distance until they reached the place where the Milk River flows into the great stream. When she was a child they had followed this northern stream rather than the Missouri. But she told the white men she knew the headwaters of the great stream well, for it was near there she had been taken prisoner. She told of mountains and canyon walls, of passes known only to her people. Of all the party, she was the only one who had ever seen the Rocky Mountains. It was late in May when the expedition had its first view of them, and it was like a dream at last come true.

But there were difficulties here, for two streams joined now to make the Missouri. Which was the one to follow? Sacajawea could not help them, for she had never seen this stream before. Instinctively she held that the south fork was the one to take.

"There are falls," she told the white men. "On the river that brings you to the land of my people there are great falls. That was the home of the Pahkee. It means Falling Water. Those people are related to the Gros Ventres, who are also the Minatarees. The south fork is the one. The north fork will take you into the land of the Blackfeet."

"I will explore," said Lewis. "Before we move the whole expedition we will discover which stream has the great falls. Then we will be sure which is the one to take."

It was not too far away. In the distance he could hear a roaring as the water passed down over the rocky drop of the river. Everyone was thrilled. It was like opening a book which one had never read. Here were the mountains such as Coronado had told about. Here were the great falls of the Missouri River that had been but a legend. When Captain Lewis returned he had rather disconcerting news. They could go no farther than the falls, for no one could go over them and live. Investigation found that there would be about eighteen miles of portage. Eighteen miles, and they would have to carry every bit of their heavy supplies all the way.

But soon the great saws were eating through the huge cottonwood trees and then cutting the trunks into wheel-like disks. Crude wagons were fashioned with these wheels, and with them the men set to work transporting the supplies past the series of falls to the spot where again the Missouri traveled in smooth content. It took a long time to make this transfer. The river had four cataracts within sixteen miles and passed down a narrow canyon with high steep walls. The roar of the waters could be heard from afar and the mistlike spray made rainbows in the sun.

The work was hard, grueling hard, and the heat was bad. The road they made with the crude wagons was rough and often filled with cactus. To add to these miseries the mosquitoes came in swarms to plague them.

To the Indian girl all this was very strange, but it was in keeping with all the other things that the white men did. They were not doing this desperately hard work for food. They risked their lives over and over again and for no apparent purpose. Often in the evening she listened to the men talking together and she wished she could understand the words they spoke. Sometimes not understanding the language of the white men seemed as much a wall to hold her back as were the high mountains that lay ahead and gave the white man so much concern. If she could only speak and be understood! But her words must always go through Charbonneau. He was cruel and unkind to her, but what would she do without him?

When he was kind he talked about many things. He told of the white men who lived far to the rising sun, in much better houses than did the Mandans. They had horses and ships and good weapons. There were people called the Spanish. She had already heard of them. It was from them long ago that her people had secured their horses. The old, old woman had told her about that once long, long ago. Charbonneau said that the Spanish had turned over a great portion of land to the French. Of course she knew the French. Was not her man a Frenchman? His boasts were empty like the whistling wind; he was jealous and deceitful. In her thoughts he was "no good." But he was her man, and he made the only link between herself and the whites because he could speak a language that she knew. So if all the French were like him they would not make good neighbors. It was well Napoleon, the great French chieftain, had needed money for his wars so that he had been willing to sell the land east of the Rockies to Chief Jefferson. She may have puzzled over money. Her people traded with beads, food, skins, horses, or squaws. But money was something else. Someday she would find out about money. But now she was going with the expedition to the great waters beyond the Rocky Mountains. What were they seeking? Was it land the white men would claim for their own? What did that mean? They could not take it back with them. It would still be there. It was all very strange!

No white man had ever passed the land held by her people. They had made friends with other tribes; the Minatarees and the Mandans had liked them. Surely her people must like them too.

There was Captain Lewis. He was very wise. He knew much about medicine. Once on the trip she had been very, very ill. Captain Lewis had known what medicine to give her to make her well. But she did not feel toward him as she did toward Captain Clark. Perhaps it was because she thought of him as she did the medicine men of her people. She was afraid of them although they drove out devils and mixed up horrible-tasting things to make one well. The medicine man was one to fear, although one would be afraid to be without him too. So she was a little afraid of Captain Lewis.

But she was not afraid of Captain Clark. He was never moody or aloof. He radiated good spirits. He understood her although there were few words that they had in common. He adored her baby, Baptiste, little Pomp. Captain Clark was large, redheaded, and kind. The men were rough, but they all had a strange feeling of responsibility for the little Indian mother. There was the huge Negro, York, Captain Clark's servant; Bratton, the hunter and gunsmith who had the first experience with the bear. Shields, hunter and iron and wood worker. Pryer and the two Field boys, Reuben and Joseph, who were never happier than when there was a daring task at hand. There was John Colter, who said civilization stifled him. He could not find enough daring adventure even in the expedition. Later he was to have an experience all his own; for he was to be the first white man to see Yellowstone Park or "Colter's Hell," as it was called. There, too, was young George Shannon, who ran away from home to join the expedition; Gass, an Irishman; Drouillard, half-breed; and Cruzatte, a skilled river man who also played the fiddle. These and the others were her friends —even Scannon, Captain Clark's dog. They were her friends and she was their friend. Each one of them knew that in time of need she would give aid to any one of them.

Like the men, she grew a little more shabby with the passing days. Her one priceless possession was the belt of blue beads that Captain Clark had given her long ago back at the Mandan village.

After the day's hard toil when the coolness of the night came whispering in, she would take little Pomp from his cradle on her back and put him down to stretch and rest. He would lie there dimpled and bronzed, gurgling softly as she greased his little body. The great men pushed about and watched humbly. No matter how hard the day, their tones were gentled as they watched the little mother with her child. Sometimes she looked into their faces and read there more than they knew. For she knew that in their thoughts her baby stood for those they loved and had left behind.

Chapter 10

Of the Same Blanket

After they had passed the rapids of the Missouri at Great Falls, their route turned south and Sacajawea began to recognize many things from her childhood days. When at last they came to a spot where the river divided into three separate channels they felt sure that they had at last come to the headwaters of the Missouri and named the place Three Forks. Here they followed the

Jefferson branch; for Charbonneau told them that it was upon this river that his squaw had been taken prisoner and made a slave by the Pahkees, later to be turned over to the Minatarees. Although the expedition had followed the Missouri, which had made a broad highway for them through this western wilderness, they had encountered no Indians along the route, but in many places they had seen signs of them. The game had grown more scarce, which showed that the native animals had gone farther down the river away from the mountains.

"You'd think the girl would show some excitement about coming back to her people," said Cruzatte as he thumbed at his fiddle one evening. "Her folks might be a thousand miles away for all she seems to care. I looked for her to get all excited when we came close to the range where she used to live. Do you remember how excited she got the first day we smelled sagebrush?"

"Uh-huh," said Patrick Gass. "She sure took on. I thought she was plumb daffy. She danced and sucked her fingers and said such strange words. Guess it was her native tongue. Anyway that no-good scallywag of a husband of hers said something to her that brought her to her senses."

"It was a sweet smell," said young Shannon. "I remember it was just after a rain and the wind came fresh and sweet with the odor. Made me think just a mite of the lavender Mother used to put among her linens. I guess no one who ever smells it will quite forget it. Perhaps it told Sacajawea that she was coming home. I've been kind of disappointed in her, too, since then. She says we are near her people. She says they know we are

90

here. We have seen signal fires, that's certain. It makes me feel skittish to think they know where we are but we don't know where they are."

"I don't know as you can blame her," said another one of the men, "when you remember how she was captured here and so many of her folks were killed. Maybe she doesn't know how bad things are with them and is almost afraid to find out. Some think she doesn't remember the past. But she hasn't acted like that."

"You're right," said young Shannon. "And I'll wager she'll be excited when she meets her people. But she isn't going to waste herself over it until the time comes. Anyone who has lived in the wilds as she has learns a lot of discipline, living with hunger and cold and enduring all kinds of hardships. They have to be pretty stoical, although she's shown such a lot of traits I never expected we'd see. Her willingness to be of help and her loyalty to us are pretty fine."

"And that's the truth," said Cruzatte. "You might give some of the credit to Charbonneau if he wasn't such a worthless whelp. But what she is, that is good; she is of herself, not from him."

They were not the only ones who were concerned as they drew nearer the place which they had sweated and worked for months to find. Captain Lewis was giving a very great deal of thought to it too. At times he was alarmed that the girl seemed to show so little interest in finding her people. True, she had given them much information. She had said, "When you go into an Indian camp you must make a great deal of noise. You must stand far off and shout so they may see you and know that you are coming. Then they will know that you are a friend. For an enemy would be sly and try to steal upon them unseen."

There was a great deal that could be done with a blanket too. A blanket signified much with the red men. Those in the same family were "of the same blanket." To spread down a blanket indicated that you wanted a friendly visit. The word "tabba-bone" meant white man. If they should meet an Indian and be able to talk with him they should say "tabba-bone" and bare their arms to show that their skin was white. Many of the Indian tribes believed the white man to be something sacred. Captain Lewis remembered all these things for the time when he should need them. He often went on scouting trips alone. But now as they neared the long-awaited danger spot he took with him a few members of the party and Drouillard, who was a half-breed and able to converse with the Indians by means of the sign language.

They left Clark and the other members of the party on a branch of the Jefferson River. Captain Lewis pondered over the idea of taking Sacajawea and it would have saved him some troubled hours if he had. But he was not sure of her. He knew a squaw had little standing among the red men. It was better to leave her in camp until he had looked over the land.

So he and his men went on together, climbing until they reached the summit. Beyond lay range after range of mountains whose rivers flowed to the Pacific. It was a moment of triumph to each one as they raised the stars and stripes, on that day of August 12, 1805, claiming the land that lay before them in the name of the United

States Government. They knew Indians were in the vicinity and that they were being watched. It was several days before they were able to approach them in the manner Sacajawea had advised, and they gave them a few gifts. Later they met a group of warriors and were welcomed, for the ones to whom they had given the presents had told of the shining ornaments they received. Three headmen stepped forward and embraced Captain Lewis and took them to the Chief, where they were seated in a circle. Lewis remembered Sacajawea's instructions to remove his moccasins before he passed the calumet to the chieftain. He lit the pipe carefully, drew a deep puff, and passed it to the chieftain. His bared feet said that if he ever broke the friendship he hoped that he would always go barefoot. Then the Chief told Captain Lewis that he would take them to their camp and they all set off together.

The Indians were dressed in skins and hides trimmed with fringe and porcupine quills. Many wore beautiful furs and others had wings or tail feathers of birds bound about their foreheads. The Chief was garbed in a buffalo robe, which was rich with embroidered quills in many colors. He also wore a collar of otter and ermine skins with pearl shells. There was no doubt they had been expecting the white men and had put on their best to welcome and impress them. In contrast the white men in their hunting and scouting costumes seemed more than ever like a different people.

Captain Lewis missed no detail of their dress and recognized that they were a proud people. There was character in the face of the chieftain. It was a great event having the white men as his guests. There was a dance that night but Captain Lewis begged to be allowed to rest. So far all had gone well, but it was not easy to rest. The dance went on and his thoughts beat through his mind. They needed help from these people. Would they give it? They must have horses. So far Drouillard had not been successful. He thought of Sacajawea. She would have been able to speak to them. But what could she do? Yet he had a strange belief that in some way she would be of even greater help than before, and at last, in that hope, he slept.

Back by the sluggish stream Captain Clark and his men were making little progress. The stream branched and they did not know which one to take, so they chose the one that was was later known as the Beaverhead. As they moved on, the stream became more shallow and harder to travel. Charbonneau complained of a sprained ankle and Captain Clark was miserable with boils. Captain Lewis had been gone for several days into an unknown land where no white man had ever been before. What could be keeping him? Had some evil befallen him and his companions? If so, that same evil might soon find them still tugging up the shallow tangled stream with their boats and supplies. What was best to do?

It was as if a cloud hung over them and yet they all tried to keep cheerful. Captain Clark drove them on. The very fact that Captain Lewis had not returned made it imperative that they push on to be near the place where he might have need of them. The one calm member of the whole expedition was Sacajawea. She took time to bathe and dress her baby. She had more time to spend with her child now. The white men liked to see him kept clean and well cared for and encouraged her to take the time to do it. He was beautiful; his body so perfectly formed, so plump and dimpled. The most beautiful papoose in all the world, she told herself. So on this day, after she had him shining and clean and well dressed, she took him on her back and joined Charbonneau and Captain Clark as they moved ahead to a little hilltop where they could see a greater distance.

And then it happened! As they reached the crest of the hill she suddenly gave a cry of joy such as they had never heard before. In that moment Sacajawea forgot all the past. There were her people! She ran to them. One was a squaw, Rabbit Ear, the friend of her childhood, the little playmate who had escaped and returned to her people. Sacajawea had never dared to think of her, for she locked the door of her mind fiercely against things that she could not change. But here was her friend, alive, alive. The wonder, the joy of it! The white men and the Indians watched together. They were both amazed. The white men had not dreamed there was such depth of feeling in this young Indian mother, and in a way they felt a little ashamed that they had doubted her. Her happiness was so genuine, so complete.

And then after the thrill of finding her friend alive, Sacajawea remembered that she had something to show them. Her baby, her beautiful papoose! She showed him with pride. How glad she was that she had groomed him so carefully that morning! No one could look at him and not know how wonderful he was and, of course, then she must call Charbonneau, the baby's father, and finally

Captain Clark had to be explained. It was an hour of triumph beyond anything that she had ever dreamed. Everyone was happy. Sacajawea wanted to ask about her brother, but she hesitated for fear they might say he was not there. Soon her people interrupted her thoughts saying they would take them to a camp where their Chief and a white man waited. Captain Clark drew a sigh of relief. That must be Captain Lewis. It looked now as if their troubles were at an end. As they turned to go on together the Indians raised their voices in song, strange song, that Sacajawea remembered as from another lifetime. It seemed to say, "All is well. No one need be fearful." Even Charbonneau and Captain Clark could feel the meaning, the wild joyous freedom that rang through the words they could not understand.

There was a joyous reunion and Lewis and Clark embraced. Lewis whispered that he was not sure the Indians were convinced they were friendly. A council was to be planned immediately and they must have Sacajawea come at once. He said he could not be sure of the Indians and to show his good faith he had even given the Chief his gun.

The council circle was made immediately in a spot sheltered by willow boughs. Sacajawea came in timidly. A council circle was no place for a squaw. This she knew and it made her fearful. But she must tell Charbonneau in Minataree the words her people spoke, so he could translate them to the Captains. When the Captains spoke, Charbonneau would repeat their words in Minataree and she would tell her people in Shoshone. She knew that outside the squaws must be talking together about her going into the council circle. She wanted to run away. But this must be done. She looked into the face of Captain Clark, her friend, her baby's friend, and she saw the tired troubled lines in his face. So she raised her head and sat straight and lithe as an arrow ready to let the words flow through her.

She said, "The white men come as friends and will do our people no harm. They are on their way to the Great Water by the setting sun. They wish to buy horses and will pay well for them. They will deal fairly. You can trust them."

While she had been speaking her eyes had been downcast, but with her last words she raised her eyes to the Chief. She stopped speaking. She stood up. The white men held their breath. What had happened to her? Could this be the quiet little Indian mother who showed no emotion? She slipped the blanket from her shoulders and threw it over the shoulders of the chieftain. Charbonneau started to cry out, but Captain Clark grabbed his arm.

"We are of the same blanket," cried Sacajawea in her native tongue. "You are my brother, my brother. You are Cameahwait. Do you not remember me?"

He looked at her in wonder. He had never expected to see her alive again after that horrible day so long ago. It was like the dead living again. For a moment he could not speak.

"I gave you my horse to escape that day," Sacajawea explained. "You were more important to our people than I. I was taken prisoner and carried far away to the Mandan village and the home of our enemies, the Gros

Ventres or Minatarees. And now I have come back with my friends and have found you again. You are a chieftain, my brother. This makes me very proud."

The ties of family are strong in the Indian and being of the same blanket is the strongest bond they know. The Chief, striving to hide his emotion and yet deeply touched, scarcely realized that the white men who watched the little drama understood what had happened without translation.

Captain Lewis rose to his feet and faced the Chief. He rejoiced with him over the return of his sister and told of their gratitude to her for the many things she had been able to do to aid the expedition. He presented the Chief with gifts some of the men had brought from their supply of stores.

Sacajawea translated the Chief's gratitude and his promise of horses and the return of their guns. He said his sister's friends were his brothers and pledged his help to them. And then some of the white hunters came in with several deer and the council broke up for a time of feasting.

At one side Captain Lewis told Clark of a terrifying experience he had been through. He had found the Shoshones the day before, but in spite of carrying out all Sacajawea's instructions they were skeptical. When morning came they feared the whole thing a plot to lead them into trouble. He knew he must get back to the boats and supplies, but they doubted him every step of the way. Had Clark not appeared soon, things might have had an entirely different ending.

"Even when you came I was fearful," he continued.

"But for the little squaw we might not have convinced them. That blanket business with the Indian is powerful medicine. To the day I die I shall not forget the Chief's face when she threw her blanket over him! I do remember Charbonneau telling something about family ties with the Indian, and the bond of brothers and sisters; but he mixed things up so badly, or fixed them to suit his fancy, that I didn't pay much attention. I'd say tonight that we owe her our lives and if the expedition does succeed she will deserve a great share of the credit."

Captain Clark nodded. He had always believed in the little squaw and he enjoyed hearing his companion voice his thoughts so accurately. Together they watched the wild joy of the tribe as they ate their fill and sang. But Sacajawea was not among the merrymakers. She had slipped out into the darkness. She had come home. But it was not the same. It could never be the same, for she had gone from it a child and returned a woman. There had been a father and a mother, but they were gone. Her only sister had died a short time before, leaving a young son to face the world without her. Only her brother, the Chief, remained of her family. When she had allowed herself to think of the old days she remembered life as it had been—she a wild slip of a girl, fleet of foot, who could ride a horse bareback like the wind. But all that was in the past. She had a child now; and she belonged to Charbonneau, a hard master. No, life would never be the same again. And then she felt that someone stood beside her. It was her friend.

"Do you remember," she whispered, "how you used to watch for wild geese? I never heard their call through all the years but I thought of you and wondered if some-day, like the geese, you would come home."

"I remember," said Sacajawea. "Always I hear them and they remind me of what I have always wanted to do. But I cannot fly. There have been times when I could not even dream of hearing them, and then something would die within me."

"Hush," her friend whispered, "here come the others."

Finding her alone with Rabbit Ear, the curious squaws crowded about. They wanted to feel the beautiful blue belt and the bright beads of her necklace. They examined her hair and the gay ribbon that bound it, and even her fringed deerskin garments and moccasins. To them the girl who had run calling after the birds had returned like a princess decked with jewels, and in such company! The "pale face," the white man, seemed quite human, now they could see him with their own eyes; but still the mystery that surrounded him caused them to stand in awe, remembering the early legends that said he had come from the spirit world.

Suddenly this moment of complete admiration was broken by an Indian who pushed through the gathering and snatched Sacajawea by the arm. He shook her roughly.

"So you have come back," he growled. "Why did you not return with Rabbit Ear? She found her way back. You are mine. I bought you from your father the day before the hunt."

At first Sacajawea was so startled she did not know what to think or do. Then she remembered the man, Little Wolf, the most disliked and unreliable member of the band. She tried to pull away from him, but he held her fast.

"It is a lie," she cried. "I say it is not so. My father would never sell me to you."

"Come with me," said the Indian. "We will go to the Chief and I can prove my words."

The squaws scattered before him as he dragged her, crying, to her brother's lodge. "Send for the Captains," she called to Rabbit Ear. "Bring Charbonneau."

The Chief, Cameahwait, heard the disturbance outside and his sister's voice calling. He did not want trouble with the white men. They had trouble enough without adding the white men to their enemies. What could have happened to his sister to arouse so much confusion? He was no more disturbed than were the two Captains as they hurried in answer to the call.

"I told you it was too good to be true," muttered Lewis. "Now if she has gotten herself in trouble all the good she has done us will be lost."

They found the Chief still in his ceremonial robes, and Sacajawea crying hysterically, "It is not true, it is not true!" An Indian was holding her by the arm.

"A villainous-looking fellow," said Captain Clark. "This doesn't look good. Where is Charbonneau? Do you suppose he is at the bottom of this? Oh, here he comes now."

Charbonneau did not wish to come, but when he saw the Captains he knew he would be needed as an interpreter. He talked with Sacajawea and learned what had taken place. She told her brother, "You know I was taken prisoner and carried far away. The Pahkees took us far north, where they met some of their people who lived toward the rising sun. They traded the squaws they had captured and I was one of them. We were taken to a far land and here the Chief sold me to this man Charbonneau, a white man, a Frenchman. Many winters ago. I now have a child. Little Wolf claims my father sold me to him. My father lost everything he had. He lost me. He lost his life. I saw it."

"I paid him for you," said Little Wolf angrily. "I was to have you after the hunt when the meat was cared for. He gave me his word. I trusted him."

"A man cannot give his word beyond his life," said Sacajawea. "When he died you had no claim upon him."

Cameahwait nodded but made no answer.

"I gave him a horse," said Little Wolf, "a beautiful horse. He rode it to the hunt. Do you remember?"

Cameahwait remembered. He had wondered about the horse his father rode that day. That told the story. It was the horse that had led his father to sell his daughter to this scoundrel. Sacajawea remembered, too, and she turned and looked at the man beside her. He must have thought her valuable to trade so beautiful a horse for her.

No one spoke. A strange silence settled about them. The Captains waited and at last Little Wolf moved uneasily. He loosened his grip on Sacajawea's arm just as a scream, shrill and terrifying, rent the air followed by a child's cries of fright. Rabbit Ear came running with little Pomp sobbing in her arms. He had wakened suddenly to find a circle of faces peering down upon him where he slept. Sacajawea held out her arms and the

102

little fellow fairly leaped into them flattening his small body against her breast, his arms clutched tightly about her neck.

Little Wolf stepped back. "I didn't know," he muttered. "I don't want her. She's another man's squaw."

The Captains hurried to their shelter and Cameahwait returned to his lodge.

"She didn't have a chance," said Captain Clark. "Whatever happened to her, it was Little Wolf here, Charbonneau there."

Sacajawea only thought of the baby in her arms, her little Pomp, and as she held him close she told herself that whatever hardships she had known he was worth all of them.

Chapter 11

The Pacific
At Last

Captain Lewis and a few men stayed with the supplies while Captain Clark, with a few helpers and Sacajawea and Charbonneau, crossed over the Lemhi Pass. Captain Clark went to explore the way ahead and left Sacajawea to talk with her people to persuade them to sell horses to the expedition. Captain Lewis, back on the Beaverhead River on the eastern slope, was busy caching the canoes and supplies they did not wish to carry on with them to the Pacific and making ready supplies they should carry with them.

Sacajawea traded shrewdly with her people and secured a dozen horses and the promise from her brother that his people would help them over the mountains with their luggage. It was already late in August and the white men were impatient to be on their way, but it took time and patience to deal with the Indians. Sacajawea would not be discouraged; she persisted. This was one thing she could do and she was determined to do it well. When everything seemed settled she discovered her brother was making plans to go to the eastern slope to hunt, thus leaving the expedition stranded. In desperation she appealed to him to be a man of his word and it had a magic effect. Before leaving, according to the custom of her people, she adopted her dead sister's child, Bazil. Although she left him with her people and did not see him again till he was a grown man, she thought of him as her son and he thought of her as his mother.

At last they were ready and on the thirtieth of August, with horses and guides, they set out on their journey down the Salmon and into the Bitter Root. The horses and the men were exhausted at night and the food grew more and more scanty. Everyone wanted a horse, but the horses had to carry the packs.

"My feet are plumb worn down to my legs," grumbled good-natured York, who usually was the last to complain. But they went on as Sacajawea knew they would. Nothing could stop them. The forests marched up and down steep ridges and into rocky beds where raced icy streams fed by mountain snows. The game grew more and more scarce. They knew hunger and cold. The wind, icy cold, tried to stop them as did the snow and the sleet.

"If there was anything else in nature that could come up and make us trouble we'd find it," grumbled one of the boys. "Remember the heat back at the falls, where we made horses of ourselves pulling wagons with solid wooden wheels. I could use a bit of that warmth now."

But things do end and this time of trouble ended too. Sacajawea saw them first—great trees! Canoe cedar! They made a camp and set about felling the trees and fashioning canoes from them. It took time. The sharp ring of the ax echoed through the valleys. Many worked at the fallen trees, cutting and burning out the centers so they could be used for boats. It was early in October when they were ready at last to set sail in their home-made crafts. This would be, the Captains both felt, the last stage of the journey.

So they set forth on the Snake River, which carried them swiftly to the stronger, deeper waters of the Columbia, on through the Columbia's gorge at the Dalles, with its falls—an experience they would never forget. But they made it safely.

It was an exciting moment when they saw a white-capped mountain. "That's the one the navigator Vancouver said could be seen from the mouth of the Columbia River," cried Captain Clark, filled with excitement. "I'll bet a coonskin cap!" They all knew a strange thrill.

Someone began to laugh; someone began to sing a rollicking song that followed from boat to boat. The end of the trail! At last! On down the stream they came. No effort was needed; the water was with them now. When the fog lifted and they saw the ocean, they knew the sounds they had heard were the roar of the breakers as they swept up on land and receded back into the waters. On a clear day in November they raised the old stars and stripes in sight of the ocean, claiming this land for the United States of America.

There was a great deal of rejoicing as they made camp that night. Men slapped one another on the back and laughed. They danced and sang, forgetting their tired bodies; for they had done the thing they had set out to do. It was accomplished! Even Captains Lewis and Clark acted like young boys. Only Sacajawea seemed unable to understand. Their mission was ended. It was for this they had come. For this they had fought every known element of nature. Just for this—a staff stuck into the ground with a bit of colored cloth at the top. What had she expected? She did not know. But certainly more than this. What good was that bit of red-and-white-striped cloth with a handful of stars in a blue field? And why should they have come so far just to bring it here?

The first thing to be done was to choose a site upon which to build a fort. Sacajawea was called in to give her opinion and it was agreed to build upon the south side of the Columbia River a few miles in from the coast. The men were up in the morning with the first feeble rays of light. Great trees were felled by those skilled with the ax while others set to work trimming the huge logs to make them ready for the builders.

The fort grew as if it were alive; log by log the walls

grew higher. Sacajawea could hardly believe the men could show such energy after the grueling trip they had made over the mountains. They bent to the task with every bit of their strength and skill. She paused in her root digging to watch them. It was as if they were driven by some great force. It was winter! Winter that came with the cold and the storm. They were running a race with winter. And so she worked hard to dig the roots, for she, too, must hurry.

The wood piles grew. The trimmings from the trees and from the logs in the building were stacked in racks close by to supply fuel for the fort during the cold. The hunters came in with game which they turned over to others who went about preparing the meat for storage and the skins for future use. It grew colder. Their clothes became soaked and partly frozen, but no one stopped; everyone kept at his task. Today was bad, but tomorrow would be no better.

Captain Clark called to Charbonneau. "Tell Janey to come and watch these natives before they carry off everything we own." For the Clatsop Indians who lived there were as curious as the Mandans had been. So Sacajawea became a policewoman whenever the Indians were about. She was quick to see when one of them picked up something and hid it away in his garments. But when Sacajawea firmly demanded that he return the article he did so willingly. These Indians were unaccustomed to the rights of ownership and had always been free to pick up what lay upon the ground. The white man was the maker of all kinds of "medicine," good and bad, and it was well to stay in his favor as the Indian squaw, who had come with the white man, warned them.

"I wonder what Janey tells them," said Captain Clark as he watched a half-frightened native produce a hammer from his deerskin garments and put it back almost tenderly where he had found it a short time before. "It doesn't matter much, so long as it does the business. Keep her at it. She is more useful in that way than in any other. And she seems to be friendly with them. They even seem to like her."

When at last the stragglers went back to their settlement, Sacajawea returned to her digging. With little Pomp huddled close to her she dug the wappatoo root to store away for winter when the ground would be frozen.

At last Fort Clatsop was ready, for they named it after the Indian tribe. A fireplace had been made for warmth. In the great room they had left one tree stump sawed to the exact height to make a table for Captain Clark. There was an abundance of firewood; the storeroom was well filled with supplies of food safely housed against intrusion by man or weather. There were hides and skins to keep them busy during the winter months preparing them for needed clothing. Even Sacajawea's roots were safe when winter came marching in.

"We did our best," said Captain Lewis. "The men worked well, every one of them. We can only hope now that it may be an easy winter with mild spells to let the hunters out to replenish our supplies. We must be very careful and use what we have wisely. There is not enough, but it will have to do."

It was well that there was work to be done. Sacajawea was familiar with preparing the hides and fashioning clothing from skins. Many moccasins must be made, as well as other garments, so that they would not be delayed for want of clothing on the homeward trip.

More and more she heard the word "home" repeated in the conversations of the men. "Home"—they said the word tenderly, lovingly. Those who had no home turned away silently. Sacajawea, watching, knew that they had memories. "Home" was a joyful word, and the warmth it brought gave them new courage and happiness. Sacajawea hugged her little son close in her arms. She did not need to wait till springtime. This was "home" to her —the best home she had ever known.

Chapter 12

Waiting Through a Winter

One morning, Sacajawea was greeted by the words "Merry Christmas, Merry Christmas." Everyone was saying it to everyone, and the few who found it hard to feel merry found little support in their companions.

"Nothing to be merry about? Why, man, we're here and now all we'll have to do is to go home in the springtime."

"Yes, just think where we were last Christmas. Ought to be mighty thankful we're here. We've done it, boys. We've done it! If Jefferson could know, I'll wager it would be his best Christmas present. Come on, Cruzatte, where's your fiddle? What in the name of all that's holy did we bring you along for?"

"Cook's fixing Christmas fixings! Going to have a real Christmas feast 'way out here sitting on the banks of the Pacific. Everywhere Christmas, even here. Folks back home are shouting 'Merry Christmas' to everyone they see. 'Merry Christmas,' folks back home. We're a-saying it to you even though you can't hear us!" A shout went up, "Merry Christmas, folks at home."

"Merry Christmas," repeated Sacajawea softly. "The birthday of God's son when a star came and stood over the manger bed where he lay. A day to be happy and to make others happy."

She had a secret, a wonderful secret. Captains Lewis and Clark had small gifts for the men and they had made gifts for one another. Sacajawea, who had never heard of "Merry Christmas" until a year ago, had a gift too. It was a nice one and she was very proud.

When she placed her bundle in the hands of Captain Clark she said the two words that were such good medicine on this wonderful day: "Merry Christmas."

Captain Clark was surprised. He had not thought that she would remember the gift-giving from the previous year. The package contained two dozen white weasel tails—a fine gift indeed. Weasel tails, such as these, were one of the most prized forms of decoration among the Indian tribes, for in winter the weasels turn white with black at the very tips of their tails. Indians prized them for decorating their ceremonial robes. She had given him what she thought was fitting for a captain or a chieftain. He could trim his jacket with them. He thanked her warmly, knowing the hours she must have spent in trapping the little creatures. Of course there had been a small gift for her today from him as well as from the men. Pomp had received many gifts from the men too. Now the youngster was playing with a set of blocks one of the men had given him made from bits of wood that had been smoothly cut and sanded.

Then Cruzatte tuned up his fiddle and began to play a tune. Soon the men were singing and their voices filled the room with Christmas music.

As the weeks passed and the food supply began to grow low, everyone seemed to know it; but no one talked about it. The men ate less now, hoping to stretch out their supplies until they were able to replenish them.

It was amazing how much food it took to feed thirty people. There was only a very little flour left. "We had no idea it would take us so long," said Captain Lewis. "If we had, I wonder if we would have had the courage to attempt it. Sometimes it is well that we do not know what lies ahead."

"Janey certainly knows how to make the most of things," said Captain Clark. "I found her breaking up the bones that the men usually throw away. She boiled them and it was amazing the quantity of fat and good food she extracted. When she is through with a thing there really isn't too much left for good old dog Scannon. The men are fine about getting out after food. They all

113

realize our predicament. It is a good thing we have been able to get some fish too. It all helps our bill of fare."

That evening the men came in very excited. Sacajawea knew from their voices that something unusual had happened. She tried to understand. There were some words that she knew and many that she could say. But when the white men became excited their words seemed to flow together. There was one word that she heard over and over. "Whale." But what was whale? She could not recall hearing the word before.

Her French trapper husband was not good at giving details and it was difficult to learn all the things she wished so very much to know. A whale, she discovered, was a monster that lived in the ocean. Whales were the largest animals in the world. The one the men had found was a small whale not yet full-grown that had been washed up on the shore. But still it was a very large animal. It was something like a fish. It lived in the water but, unlike fish, had to come to the surface for air. Some of the meat was good to eat. The fat would be useful in many ways and even its bones were useful, for they were strong and supple.

In her corner by the fire Sacajawea pondered over all she had heard. To think that one of the greatest animals in the world lay not far away! Perhaps none of her people had ever seen a whale. Perhaps no Mandan had ever seen one, and certainly no Minataree. But she, Sacajawea, was going to see it! She would see the whale and she would see the Great Water too.

Each day when new parties went down, Sacajawea was left behind. Soon she came to understand that

Charbonneau was making no effort to have her taken along. Perhaps he did not wish her to go. So she set to work to make Charbonneau understand that she must go and he must help her. At last the Frenchman went to Captain Clark and told him of her desires. He did it reluctantly, and showed no interest in having her request granted.

"She acts very bad," he told the Captain. "She cries and says she is badly treated. She says she has done all she could to help and she wants to see the whale and the great water. There is much to do here—moccasins to make, skins to prepare. There is no need for her to go. You tell her to behave and stay here where she belongs."

"Bring her here," said Captain Clark. "It is a long cold trip and perhaps I can persuade her to give it up."

But when "Janey" came he knew she was going to see the whale. If they did not take her she would go herself. She had not come all this distance to be stopped by a little cold and discomfort when something so fascinating lay so near. In a way he was surprised at her determination and earnestness. For the first time he had a little flash of understanding of this wild young creature— her urge to see what lay beyond the next hilltop, and the next. This was the living thing within her that kept her spirit alive and eager. The whale, the ocean—they, too, were hilltops.

"Tell her," he said, turning to Charbonneau, "that a trip shall be arranged. You and I, Charbonneau, and three or four of the men will go tomorrow. If she wishes so much to see these things she should not be denied."

It was a dark day when they set out and the ocean

looked cold and gray. The great waves came rolling in, racing high upon the sandy beach and then slowly receding before the next that came plowing in like mighty steeds with white foam upon their crests. White sea gulls fluttered over the waves, sometimes riding out on the receding waves. It was fascinating to the Indian girl. She watched the motion of the water and seemed to forget that she was not alone.

At last she had seen it, the Great Water at the setting sun. It was more than she had ever dreamed of seeing back in the days when she worked with the bone hoe at the bend of the river where the Minataree made his camp. The Great Water! There was water as far as the eye could see and farther, still farther! She had heard of the Great Water, for the knowledge of it had passed from tribe to tribe; but she had never expected to see it.

She was to marvel still more at the monster of the sea. All the men said it was a small whale, but to her it was the largest animal she had ever seen. And it lived in the water! The water must be very deep to have such huge creatures make it their home. She stood and looked and wondered. If the whale came from the water, then what other great creatures must be in its depths? It must hold wonders beyond anyone's dreams. She studied the whale carefully so that she might be able to describe it to her people when she returned and tell Pomp about it when he was old enough to understand. It would make much food for them, that she could see. How glad she was that she had been able to come and see it! Captain Clark had been kind to make the trip. Now she had seen the Great Water and the whale. She had made a mental picture of them, deep in her mind, that she would not forget. She had seen so much, so much! She thought of the squash vine and smiled. She had not taken root. She would never take root! And for one startled instant she remembered she was returning to that life when springtime came. But she shook away the thought. No, she would never take root. She would always be free. She stumbled a little as she turned reluctantly when the men called, at last, that they must be back at the fort before dark. She was thinking of the long trail she had followed, and she knew there would be other hilltops!

Darkness was drawing the curtains of the day when they reached the fort. They could smell the good warm food before they reached the doorway and hear Pomp's shrill cry of glee as he saw them coming. He shouted and danced and Captain Clark scooped him up in his strong arms and perched him on his shoulder.

"We couldn't take you, young man," he said. "Your mother will have to tell you about the whale and the Pacific Ocean."

Sacajawea smiled. Here were warmth and comfort. Here was her child well and happy. The men were in a good mood and Cruzatte's fiddle sang a merry tune.

As the flour grew less and less in their storehouse, Sacajawea began to save her portion of bread and hide it away in a safe place. Their supply would not last until the springtime and little Pomp would need bread. She had spent most of her life without it and so could easily set aside her share for him. He might never again taste such good food. They were now having very little but fish. Fish—morning, noon, and night!

"Fish once in a while is good," said one of the men, "but as a steady diet it is terrible."

"A lot better than nothing," said another. "Ought to be glad we have fish. If we didn't we could go hungry. But have you noticed Captain Clark? He isn't feeling so well. I've watched him. He just can't seem to down the stuff, although he doesn't say a word."

It was true. Captain Clark was not feeling well. He couldn't bear the thought of fish. The men became anxious about him and did their best to prepare the unwanted food in different ways to make it more appetizing. But he couldn't taste it.

"If I could just have some real food for once to settle the strange aversion my digestion has for fish," he told Captain Lewis, "I think I could carry on. Everything in me rebels against the food. I'm ashamed, but I can't help it."

"Look through the supplies and see if there is meal of any kind among our stores," Captain Lewis told the men. "We had our supplies packed in different bales so if we lost a bale we would not lose all of any one necessary thing. It might be there is still a small bit of meal packed among other things."

The men looked but could find nothing. Sacajawea heard of the search. She knew where there was a small store of dry bread—dry bread that had been her portion that she had saved for her little son.

She looked at little Pomp. He was well and strong and plump. But if she did not keep it for him he might never again taste such food. She could not think of giving it up. But little thoughts came nibbling when she tried to shut them out. The Captain was sick. Her baby was well. But the food was hers! One side of her said "No." The other said "You must." She could not sleep. It was like a battle going on in her mind, round and round. "Pomp doesn't need it; Captain Clark does.". . .

Captain Clark was startled one morning to find Sacajawea bending over him, and in her hand was a piece of bread. He looked at her unbelieving. He must be dreaming. It couldn't be bread. To have bread brought to him now was as much a miracle as the manna he remembered reading about in the Bible.

"Bread, Janey? Where did you get it?" he asked her.

She seemed to read his thoughts and answered them in the few simple English words she had learned. "Mine —I keep for Pomp. Eat; you need most."

She watched him eat. He did not wolf it down as she had expected him to do. But he ate slowly, tasting to the full each tiny crumb. "Wonderful," he whispered. "Delicious. How I needed it!" It seemed to have a miraculous effect upon him and he slept quietly and seemed rested and refreshed when he wakened. He was to remember always how good those few dry bits of bread tasted, and he was to remember always that she had given him what she had saved for her child. But she thought no more about it. She had only done what had to be done.

Now that she had learned to recognize another's need, she found there were other times when she must make sacrifices. One day she heard the men telling of a trader who possessed a robe made of a beautiful pair of matched sea-otter skins, but he would part with them for only one thing—blue beads. The blue beads, like the flour and meal, were gone. These people of the western tribes were fascinated with blue beads. They were the only beads in which they were interested and the only form of trinket they desired.

"If we had only known they wanted blue beads we could have brought them a lot easier than some of the stuff we did bring," Captain Clark said. "I'd love to take back those matched skins. They are beauties. They'd be the prize of our whole collection. But we can't, for we haven't a blue bead left."

Sacajawea understood a good deal of what he said. Her hand moved to her waist and her fingers held fast the blue-bead belt. Charbonneau would take it from her, she knew, if he wished blue beads. But Captain Clark would not. Captain Clark had given them to her long ago when Pomp was born, and he would not take them back even to buy the precious matched skins. That night Cruzatte played his fiddle and little Pomp, keeping step to the music, danced on his toes Indian-fashion, setting the whole camp into a shout of appreciation. Captain Clark caught the little boy up in his arms.

"Come, Cruzatte," he called. "Another tune for my little dancing boy."

As he put the child down, Sacajawea saw the baby raise adoring eyes to the Captain's face while his tiny feet kept time to the rollicking voice of the fiddle. She turned away. What did the fiddle say? "Blue beads, blue beads, blue beads." She clutched her belt. It was hers— hers—her very own!

She found Captain Clark alone at his tree-stump table working on his reports and she laid the beautiful belt before him. He looked up puzzled.

"Take," she said simply. "Trade."

He knew what she meant. He knew how she loved the beads, but the robe was important for his collection. He thanked her, and her face glowed at his words of praise. He found among his supplies a blue coat that he gave her. Her delight made him feel less guilty for taking her prized beads. It was the first garment she had ever possessed that was not made from skins.

Chapter 13

Homeward Bound

She saw the springtime coming. She watched for all
the signs known so well to her people. Winter to her
was like a monster that held the world in its clutches,
and bit by bit its icy fingers loosened their grip as
springtime came. The ice broke on the river and the
water beneath began to move. It grew stronger from
the rippling little streams that joined it. Life began to
flow. The sap crept up into the tree trunks and branches.
Birds, always too optimistic, came back, still trembling

a little in the cold but knowing spring was coming. Springtime always fascinated Sacajawea, but the change it brought to the men who had wintered together at Fort Clatsop was even more wonderful than the change that had come in nature.

Each one was filled with a new energy. The camp bustled with life. Boats were made ready for a trip up the stream and in them they packed all their precious possessions. On March 27, 1806, they set sail at last for home.

It was upstream work now, but they did not mind. They bent to their oars and laughed and sang. They were going home, home! "Do you remember when we came?" they asked one another. "The river was with us then."

But when they reached the Dalles at the portal of the great gorge of the Columbia they gave up the boats and decided to use horses. There were falls, many of them. A clever boatman can manipulate falls going down, but going up the stream is a different story. They found some of the horses they had left with Indians the preceding fall, and secured horses from other tribes. Wherever they went the Indians were friendly when they saw Sacajawea, and she was very valuable to the expedition during this part of the journey. It seemed as if some member of the scattered Shoshone people could be found almost everywhere they went. She would hear Charbonneau's call—"Come squaw, tell them"—and would hurry to see what new member of her people they had discovered. Among the Walla Walla Indians there was a squaw who had been taken prisoner from a tribe on the Missouri River and she still spoke the Shoshone language.

Sacajawea greeted her. "We are friends," she said. "These people will do you no harm. Help us find our horses and tell us the best trail to take over the mountains. My people have gifts for you."

Then the tribe crowded about them as Captains Clark and Lewis passed out a few trinkets. These people had never before seen a white man and they stood in open-mouthed wonder.

As time passed, many Indian people were met and the supply of gifts became low. The men sometimes cut buttons from their coats and gave them to these people who had never before seen a button!

"Sacajawea is good medicine," the men said, laughing. "Here we go walking through this country almost without concern and she sets all the fears of these strange tribes at rest. We are lucky to have her. They know we are not on a raid when they see her with us."

And so they went on, meeting more and more Indian tribes and even spending some time at an Indian village on the Clearwater River. It was very lovely there. The snow was still too deep in the mountains to attempt to cross. It was not until the thirtieth of June that they came to the mouth of the Lolo River, where they had camped on the way to the Pacific. It was now three months since they had left Fort Clatsop near the mouth of the Columbia River.

It was planned to have the party divide in order that they might explore more territory. They wished to find the best and easiest ways to cross the continent. Captain

Lewis would go to Great Falls, covering more territory than when they had come west, while Captain Clark would go on and recover supplies which they had cached on their westward journey on the Beaverhead, on by boat to Three Forks, then the headwaters of the Yellowstone River at the point where it joined the Missouri. The men would be divided into the two expeditions and they would all meet at the junction of the Missouri and Yellowstone.

Sacajawea was happy when she found that she and Charbonneau were to be in Captain Clark's party. Early the next morning they set out.

"From here on, Janey," he said to Sacajawea, "you'll have to do a good bit of the leading. I hope you remember."

She nodded.

"She remembers," Charbonneau translated for her. "Been here with her people. Will take you to the place where you buried your supplies."

And she did. There were the canoes and the supplies, still in very good condition, in the cache at the headwaters of the Beaverhead.

It was easy now. The canoes drifted along on the stream. They all remembered when they had come up this stream, fighting every inch of the way through the shallow waters. At last they were at the spot where the three rivers, the Jefferson, the Gallatin, and the Madison joined hands at Three Forks to make the beginnings of the mighty Missouri River. On this return trip Sacajawea did not see her people, but her thoughts were often with them.

Now they would change their course. Captain Clark was glad to have passed through the trip down the Jefferson, for it was filled with memories for him and he was not likely to forget the uneasiness they had known as they had gone westward over this route. It was a much better thing to have behind one than ahead. When he thought of "Janey" he felt even more glad that it was past. He wondered how it affected her, for she had not spoken or given sign in any way of what might have been in her thoughts.

At Three Forks the party divided, several going on to Great Falls but about half the party going on with Captain Clark to find the headwaters of the Yellowstone River. Sacajawea led the way. It was the last time that she would be the one to say "Go this way," and then prove that she knew and had chosen well. She took them through a mountain pass known as Bozeman Pass. The men respected her judgment and had no fear of following her directions. So they came safely to the headwaters of the Yellowstone River. Here they made canoes and set out down the river to the junction with the Missouri, where they were to meet Captain Lewis and the rest of the expedition. They found Captain Lewis and his men already there, and the strong Missouri River carried them quickly to the Indian village.

It was like an awakening to suddenly know it was over—all over. Sacajawea could hardly believe it as she stepped from the boat with the Indians crowding around her. The boats had sped downstream. It was over too soon. No more would she be a guide to lead the way, to point to a cleft in a mountain ridge and say, "We can

go through there." No more rising each morning with
a new trail stretching out ahead. The thoughts within
her frightened her. It was like a wild bird beating its
wings against a cage.

Captain Clark called her and Charbonneau and they
talked about the future. "Will you come on with us?"
he asked Charbonneau, but the Frenchman shook his
head. He knew there was no place for him among the
white men. He liked the Indian life. He would be quite
an important person after this long journey. No, he
would be happy here. The Captain paid Charbonneau
five hundred dollars as wages. It seemed a fortune to
him. When a trader came again he would have money
for trading equipment and tobacco.

"Let me take my little dancing boy," Captain Clark
said, putting his hand on little Pomp's head. "I will raise
him like a white boy and give him every opportunity.
An education—all the things he can never have here."

Sacajawea could not understand all his words, but she
understood enough. She reached out both arms and
drew the little fellow close to her as she shook her head.
They told her good-by, and when they left her she took
little Pomp in her arms and held him close and warm
against her. He was better than the hilltops. She couldn't
let him go. She watched the boats move away, standing
there until they disappeared, Pomp's warm little hand
held firmly in her own.

As she turned back to find Otter Woman and her little
son, Toussaint, she suddenly felt the old desire. She
would go on. Someday she and Baptiste and Charbonneau would go down the river into a new world.

The canoes moved swiftly down the stream of the Missouri River, but the men felt a strange uneasiness.

"Hated to leave that little squaw," said one. "Still can see her standing there with little Pomp by her side. You know, she did us a heap of good. Remember how she kept after that brother of hers and just made him sell us horses and help us. She knew how to handle him. But most squaws would have said, 'The Chief is going hunting.' They wouldn't have thought they could make him change his mind. What the Chief said was orders, but not with that little squaw; and she didn't give up easy, either."

"I know what you mean," said his companion. "She's an Indian, every bit of her; but she has fine stuff in her. For what she knows, she did her best. She wasn't afraid. She was loyal. You could depend on her. Three mighty fine qualities a lot of white folks don't have."

"I heard Captain Clark offer to take them with us," said another, joining the group. "He offered to take them all and, when Charbonneau said he wanted to stay there, he said he'd take the boy and educate him like a white boy. You should have seen the little squaw. Made me think of a mother partridge when her chicks are in danger. She gathered the little fellow to her and looked daggers at the Captain. I'll be bound if she didn't. Nope, she wouldn't let the boy go. I've heard that's one thing a Shoshone mother won't do—be separated from her child. So they are all staying back there at the Indian village. She has a lot of spunk."

But Captain Clark was having the hardest time with his thoughts. He could still see her as she clutched the child to her. It was almost as if her best friend had turned upon her, trying to take her most precious possession.

"I was stupid," he told himself. "I should have known she would not let the boy go. How could she know what I was offering to the child? Education means nothing to her. It was almost as if I had accepted all her help through the long journey and then at last tried to rob her."

"But what good could it do to bring her to St. Louis?" asked Captain Lewis. "As long as she sticks with that worthless Charbonneau, life is going to be pretty bad. And I see no other way for her. After all, she is an Indian. She will soon forget the things that you praised in her and which she developed through her association with the white man. She will go back to the primitive ways of her people. No, Clark, forget it. I feel our trip was bound to be a success and she was there to help us when the time came. When a thing is right, a way is provided."

"Perhaps you are right," said Captain Clark. "I wish I could feel that my obligation was ended. I don't know that taking her to St. Louis would do any good, but we could at least see she wasn't hungry. We have seen a good bit of the red men, you and I. We know that as a people they are rovers. The Mandans are an exception, and the Minatarees are somewhat like them although they travel farther than the Mandans. Janey's people are hedged in somewhat by circumstances, but still they move up and down the valleys with no permanent abode. Janey has that trait, but it is more entrenched. There is more determination behind it. She's learned to see a thing through when she wants it. She's not like her people, who fish till they get tired and then do something else. She has more purpose and doesn't give up easily. But to me she is a friend. A man couldn't walk off and leave a faithful dog that befriended him, and even saved his life, without a pang, I think, especially in such conditions as we have left her. I'm a sentimental fool, I suppose; but I can't do it, Lewis. I'm going to send a messenger back with a letter and tell that worthless scoundrel, Charbonneau, that I will see he has work and a place to live if he will come on to St. Louis. I will at least have more self-respect if I make an effort to help them; and perhaps I can erase that look of fright I saw on her face, for the first and only time. What I said to her I meant in all kindness, but she did not understand. Perhaps even now she mistrusts me."

"Have your own way," said Captain Lewis with a shrug. "I am grateful, but we paid Charbonneau well."

"There are some things you can never pay for," said Captain Clark dryly—and he went off to write the note he had suggested, and sent it back by one of the men.

Chapter 14

Down the Missouri

Otter Woman and her little son, Toussaint, were still at Charbonneau's lodge when he and Sacajawea returned. Every day was the same and it seemed to Sacajawea as if the long trip were just a dream. But Charbonneau suddenly found himself important, for those who had become bored at his oft-repeated older stories listened eagerly to what he had to tell them now. They did not believe all he said and often let him know

that they thought his stories a part of his imagination—
sometimes even laughing uproariously as if it were a
great joke! The story of the whale affected them in this
way, and then Charbonneau would send for his young
squaw. "Tell them," he would demand.

"Oh, it is true!" she would say with such earnestness
that for a moment they would almost believe her. The
whale story was their favorite and they often asked for
it. It always sent them into gales of laughter. Charbonneau and Sacajawea came to accept this attitude, for,
after all, it was a real achievement to cause so much
merriment.

Winter came early that year and the wolves of hunger
and cold made life difficult. Although they prepared for
winter, after a fashion, there was never enough and long
before spring came again the supply would be exhausted.
Sacajawea, remembering the winter at Fort Clatsop,
thought hungrily of the fish that had become so dis-
tasteful to them as a steady diet. How good it would
taste now! Charbonneau grumbled over the shortage of
food as she had never known him to do before. It was a
good sign and she guessed that he secretly planned to
make a change before another winter was upon them.

When she could, she spoke in praise of Charbonneau's
ability as an interpreter and it was not long before he
found that he had gained a reputation which brought
him new respect. All this seemed to arouse within him
a spark of ambition that kindled into a feeble flame.
When spring came and a party of traders passed that
way he joined them as an interpreter.

Sacajawea and Otter Woman were left with plenty of

work to do, for there were skins to dress and clothing to make for their own use and to sell. When Charbonneau returned he seemed like a different man. He was in a great hurry and as ill-natured as ever, but he had plans! He was going to St. Louis, for he had heard that a great fur market had opened there. Captain Clark was there, too, and he had promised to help him if he would come and bring his family. The Captain would know how to go about finding the work he wanted to do, he reasoned. Of course the boy would have to go to school, but he was too young now. That would not be for a long time. So he demanded that his squaws make ready.

That night Sacajawea looked up at the stars in the velvety darkness. It was true, it was true! At last there would be more hilltops, more and more and more. The days of the squash vines were over, she told herself, and now her longings were to be fulfilled!

Late in August, Captain Clark was surprised by the arrival of Charbonneau and his family in St. Louis. He greeted them warmly.

"And here is Pomp, my little dancing boy," he said eagerly, reaching out his arms. But the little fellow hid his face against his mother. "He has forgotten me," said the Captain sadly. Charbonneau turned to reprove the child, but the Captain held out his hand. "No, how could he remember? He was so small when he saw me last and it is a year ago. One day"—and he smiled at the little fellow who peeped at him with one eye from the folds of his mother's buckskin dress—"one day he will dance for me again."

Sacajawea bent and whispered to the child and he

looked into her face for an instant and then stepped out
into the room and began to dance with tiny knees bent,
toes barely touching the ground, in perfect rhythm. The
Captain clapped his hands.

"Wonderful," he said as the little fellow ran to him.
He lifted him into his arms. "Tell me about yourselves,"
he said, finding a chair for Charbonneau as Sacajawea,
Otter Woman and her little son sat upon the floor. "How
did you come and what are your plans?"

"I thought I'd try it down here," said Charbonneau.
"Been out with some traders and they say this is the
place to get in touch with the fur companies. I want a
job as interpreter. My squaw still thinks you will send
the boy to school. We came down the Missouri on a
barge with some trappers. Just got in."

"I'll keep my word," said the Captain. "I've a place
that is vacant right now. I let traders use it between
trips sometimes. You'll have a roof over your heads.
We'll make arrangements for the boy to go to school as
soon as he is old enough. Have to know something more
than dancing, young fellow," he said as he put the child
down.

As they went together to see the new home, Charbonneau told of their trip down the Missouri. He ignored
his family and it was only when Captain Clark spoke
directly to Sacajawea that she was given any opportunity to join in the conversation. Then her fingers flew
like small brown birds, he thought, as she tried to sup-
plement with the sign language when her stumbling
English and French failed her.

It was a beautiful place to live, or so it seemed to

Sacajawea. When they reached the log cabin and the Captain opened the door, there was a roof—and a floor and a window! On the walls were nails on which to hang their clothing. Some rough shelves hung on one wall, and a small stone fireplace in one corner would give them warmth when the days grew cold. She looked about it with delight. Such a wonderful place! It was even finer than the Mandans'.

"There is plenty of wood," said the Captain. "And I'll send over some buffalo meat. They've just brought some in. Be a good idea to dry some of it so you'll have supplies if you go trapping. Even though there is plenty of game it's a good idea to carry some with you should you have bad luck. I'll see what I can do for you in the way of a job, Charbonneau. I'd like to see you get a little tract of land and settle down. You could raise most of your food; and you are getting older, you know."

"I want to be an interpreter," said the Frenchman. "I might get some land, but I don't think I'd like it."

"Well, remember this. I'll try to help you on condition that you have the boy here go to school. That is the reason for such a plan as I suggested—so you wouldn't be dragging your family all over the country when you should be here."

"I promise he'll be here," said Charbonneau.

Sacajawea tried to thank the Captain, but he would not listen. "Take care of the boy, Janey," he said with a smile, using his old nickname for her, "and teach him a new dance."

The two squaws worked for days drying the meat that was sent to them. They cut it into very narrow thin strips and hung it in the sun to dry. It seemed an endless task and Otter Woman grew tired.

"There will be more," she said. "Why bother?"

But Sacajawea kept on. The time might come when they would need it. It was well to have a supply. Her hands were blistered from cutting with the knife, but at last it was finished. Then she set out to see the things she had all her life wished to see.

She carried Baptiste. He was too big for the papoose board. Bending down, she lifted him upon her back with his arms about her neck. Then she drew her blanket around him so that it supported him and she could hold him safely.

St. Louis was a young town, only about twenty years older than Sacajawea. It began life as a French trading post and only in the last four years, since the United States had acquired it from France with the Louisiana Purchase, had it made much growth. At one time in its history it had belonged to Spain, and now many of the people from these two countries still lived on the banks of the great Mississippi River. There were also a few from England, and Indians from many tribes, half-breeds, Americans, and Negro slaves. As she watched them and learned something about them, her wonder grew. Here were so many people from so many "beyonds" gathered together in this one place! There were about a thousand people living in the little town.

She was fascinated with the white squaws, who were called "women" or "ladies." Their clothes were different and their hair was worn piled on top of their heads and gave them such a dignified air. As she watched them at their work she realized that the white women had an enemy—an enemy with which they waged eternal battle. Day after day, all the time, they fought dust and dirt! They cleaned and scrubbed! They scrubbed their homes; they scrubbed their clothes; they fought with brooms and cleaning rags; they scoured with ashes, but the battle was never won. It went on and on and on. As she watched them work she felt a bit sorry for them. Perhaps, someday, they would become as wise as her people and know that dust and dirt were just a part of life— one of the unpleasant things one endured like mosquitoes or the cold or even hunger. Only these passed away, but the dust and dirt lasted always.

She watched the white women cook, and the wonderful odors that came from their kitchens made her hungry. Surely the Indian could learn much from the white women's cooking. She saw them eating together as they sat at a table. She had seen knives, forks, and spoons, for the Captains had them; but they were hardly necessary, she thought. Her people ate with their fingers. Of course it would be well for Baptiste to learn to use utensils, for he was going to school and would someday be a great man. She liked their houses. They were the finest she had seen, even finer than the one Captain Clark had lent them. They had bedrooms with beds that they covered with many strange pieces of cloth, two pieces of something smooth and white that they must sleep between. It would be very nice, but she loved her blanket and there was no better bed than the hard ground. It rested one.

At night she would think over all the things that she

had seen and learned. She knew about the rivers now. The little ones joined hands and made bigger ones and went on and on while others joined them and at last they reached the Great Water.

She had much time to explore, for Charbonneau joined a trapping expedition and was away for a long time. She was amazed by the stores, for they held so many things for people to buy—things she had never seen before. Some traded furs for their purchases, but many paid with money. Money was magic—white man's magic! A small coin that was not really good for anything could be used to buy wonderful things at the store. She found it hard to understand about money. She made moccasins and brought them to the store to sell. With the money she received she bought things that she needed. She would ask "Do I have enough?" and the storekeeper would tell her. She always bought one thing at a time and paid for it before she bought anything else. It was wonderful to find she had some money left after she had paid for a purchase! Sometimes the storekeeper became uneasy and once he spoke to her sharply. When she answered him in French he was surprised. She told him of the Indians at Fort Clatsop and how she had guarded the building for Captains Lewis and Clark. She was proud and she knew better than to take things that did not belong to her. After that he was always kind to her and tried to help her understand about money and the many things in his store that she did not know.

She told Otter Woman of all she saw and begged her to come down, but Otter Woman was shy and timid. It was all so strange and new to her. When she did go she

only wanted to sit out of the way in the shade of a
building where she could watch the passers-by and
could draw her shawl over her face if anyone seemed
to notice her. She begged Sacajawea to tell her of the
many things she saw.

"I will tell you one of the strangest things," said Sacajawea. "The white man—the best white man—has only
one wife."

"Is he so poor he cannot afford more than one?" Otter
Woman asked.

"He is not poor. He could buy many if he wished. He
has only one because that is the way of the white man.
When they live with us, though, sometimes they take
our ways as has Charbonneau."

"It is the best way," said Otter Woman. "I would not
like to do all the work. I am glad to have you help me
with it."

"There is more," said Sacajawea. "He did not buy his
wife. White men do not buy their wives. Women are not
sold. A white woman does not become a man's wife
unless she wishes to."

Otter Woman shook her head. "It would cause a great
deal of trouble, I think. Our way is the best."

Sacajawea made no reply. She was thinking how her
father had sold her to Little Wolf. At last she spoke.
"Some of the white men have slaves—people with black
skins, like York. Their wives are black too. They are
servants of the white man. Only among our people are
we called 'squaws'; the white man says 'women' or
'ladies.' "

139

"I like the name 'squaws' best," said Otter Woman. "It means something."

At that moment Charbonneau arrived from his trapping expedition. He had made plans to go on another trip and was taking them with him. They were leaving at once. They knew how impatient he was, so they scurried to gather the things they must take. Charbonneau led the way, with his two squaws following laden down with packs upon their backs and the two small boys running at their sides.

It was three years before they returned to St. Louis to stay. It had grown during their absence and had become incorporated as a town with a population of about twelve hundred residents. Little Pomp had grown, too, and now it was time for him to go to school. He was to be called Baptiste, for he was going to a white man's school and should have a white man's name. Charbonneau had a good job as interpreter with one of the larger fur companies and was taking Otter Woman and her son with him and leaving Sacajawea with her boy while he was in school.

It was lonely at the little log cabin. Sacajawea had looked forward to the day when her son should go to school and yet she had no idea what it really meant. He brought home papers with marks on them that puzzled her. How could this help Baptiste to become a great man? She would have left and taken her boy with her but for her faith in Captain Clark, who thought it was a good thing for Baptiste. He should know, she told herself; so they would stay. School was no doubt "white man's magic"!

Chapter 15

White Man's Magic

During the hours that Baptiste was in school Sacajawea explored the surrounding country. She loved the river. Sitting on the bank, she watched the river bring the hilltops to her. It was an ever-changing picture—boats, barges, canoes, rafts, and crafts of all kinds moved up and down the stream and every incoming boat or barge seemed laden with silken treasure. The huge supplies amazed her—buffalo robes from the plains; beaver, mink, and marten pelts from the streams and swamps; and many other skins in varying quantities. What a slaughter! The thought startled her. The animals were being destroyed! Nature could never keep up with the toll that was being taken. Famine would walk in the land unless . . . unless the Indian accepted the white man's way of life and learned to make his living from the soil. Once her people killed for necessary food and clothing; now they killed for more skins to trade for a gay blanket or a handful of beads.

Charbonneau returned after many months only to leave again in a short time with another expedition. He asked Sacajawea to go with him but dared not force her because of his promise to the Captain. According to the custom of her people a mother could not be separated from her child. If Sacajawea went with him she would take Baptiste, this he knew, and that would displease the Captain. So he went off with Otter Woman, leaving Sacajawea behind. The time came when he was gone longer than ever before and traders returning from the north told of a war between the United States and Great Britain, the War of 1812. They said the British fur traders were encouraging the Indians to attack American trading posts and forts and it was believed Charbonneau had become involved. The years slipped away one after another and Baptiste grew into a sturdy young boy. They began to wonder if Charbonneau would ever return. There were rumors that he had gone again to the Minatarees and some believed he had been killed in the Indian uprisings.

At last Sacajawea grew tired of the river, the boats, the barges, and the people. She was restless and in the still of the autumn nights she sometimes thought she heard the call of the wild geese that all her life had aroused such desire within her. But now she could not answer them. She was not going anywhere! She would not go although her whole being longed to be out and away. Then she looked down upon Baptiste as he slept. He was her hilltop, she would tell herself. She would watch him grow and develop and at last become a great man who could help her people. Sometimes she cried out against it, but she would not sacrifice duty for desire.

One day Captain Clark sent for her. "Janey," he said, "when trouble comes we all have to do our part. There is a new load for you to carry. A boat has just come in with two children, the boy Toussaint and a baby girl. Their mother, Otter Woman, died on the way here of putrid fever. We do not know the whereabouts of Charbonneau. I will legally adopt these children and provide for their needs, but I want you to take care of them." Sacajawea nodded.

She carried the baby to her cabin, with Toussaint clinging to her. She knew the baby was very frail and something warned her that she would soon go to her mother. "There will soon be another little white flower on the mountainside," she thought. She did her best for the child, and the Captain sent a woman to help her care for it; but it was too late. Captain Clark made the arrangements for her burial and Sacajawea, Baptiste, and Toussaint grieved for Otter Woman's child.

Their task now was to comfort the boy Toussaint, who

had known such fright when left alone without his mother through the terrible days of her illness and death.

"I have three sons now," Sacajawea told him, "you, Baptiste, and Bazil, my dead sister's boy. He lives far away in the Lemhi Valley. Someday we will go and see him."

"Can we go now?" he begged.

"No, you must go to school with Baptiste. You must try hard to learn. Baptiste can sign his name. That is wonderful. He can read from a book. He can count and he is teaching me to count. I shall learn so I can count money; and you shall learn, my Toussaint. Someday you may become a great and wise chief."

So happiness came to them again. She often took the boys to the river to learn the many things a boy should know. They learned to swim and paddle through the water on rafts they built themselves. They learned how to recognize tracks of animals, how to use the bow and arrow, and how to ride a pony as their people did in the far mountains of the west.

One day the boys came home very excited. "Something wonderful is to happen," they told Sacajawea. "It comes tomorrow!"

"It is a boat," said Baptiste, "a boat that has no sail or oars but moves."

"No," said Sacajawea. "No!"

"You shall see," they told her. "It is a steamboat! You know steam. Steam rises up when water boils."

"It is strong when it is shut up," said Toussaint, eager to have a share in the story. "Our teacher told us about it. It makes power. Power like a man working! Man has harnessed the steam like a horse!"

"I do not understand," said Sacajawea.

"But you shall see," the boys told her.

They could hardly wait for morning and quite early a crowd gathered at the levee. Everyone wanted to see the new wonder, the steamboat! They saw it coming. It was true; there were no sails, no oarsmen bending their backs over their oars. It was a magic boat that sailed by an unseen hand! People danced and sang. It was unbelievable, but it was true. They could see it with their own eyes. There were so many things these people had that were new and wonderful to Sacajawea. For the first time she shared with them the joy of something that was new to all. It seemed to build a bond between them. She looked at the ship. "White man's magic," she said to herself, and she joined in the shouting.

"Hurrah for the steamship, the first on the Mississippi."

This day, August 2, 1817, marked an era of development for the little town of St. Louis, making it the most important point in the settlement of this great region.

Charbonneau returned at last and with him he brought a new squaw, Eagle. It was no surprise to his family. They expected it and were grateful that she was good-natured and pleasant. She seemed glad to join them and to have help in carrying out Charbonneau's demands.

He hardly knew his family, for the two boys had become sturdy teen-age youths and Sacajawea, who should, he thought, begin to look old, was even more attractive in her early thirties than when she was a young girl. She had developed a gracefulness and dignity that few Indian women possessed. Her carefully made Indian costume and glossy black hair showed a pride in her appearance. During the years spent in St. Louis with the boys she had escaped the life of slavery and drudgery that would have been her lot had she gone with Charbonneau, for it was such a life that robbed the women of her race of their youth and turned them into old women while they were still young. She had developed into the full bloom of womanhood that few Indian squaws ever attained. Charbonneau at once admired and resented it. He knew she was different, but he was too dependent upon Captain Clark to risk doing what he would have liked to do. The very fact that she had stayed in St. Louis instead of going with him festered in his mind. When, he asked himself, did a squaw dictate what was to be done? But he remembered the warnings of long ago from Captain Clark and he knew they were still in force. His two sons had grown and would take her part against him, but Sacajawea gave him little opportunity to become angry with her. She did not boast or seem to know that she was in any way different from Eagle. She shared the work and even did more than was required of her, and Charbonneau knew that her work was better than that of his other wife. She was kind and tactful; she knew when to speak and when to keep silent.

Chapter 16

A Wanderer

In summer they went together on trapping and trading trips where the boys learned much from their father concerning the fur-bearing animals and the care and value of their skins. Sacajawea loved these trips even though Charbonneau was unreasonable in his demands and often almost brutal to his two squaws. When fall came she returned with the two boys to St. Louis, where they went back to school again, and Charbonneau and Eagle joined a trading expedition going up the Missouri River.

147

One summer they all went with Charbonneau to a small settlement owned by a large fur-trading company near the mouth of the Kaw River, and Charbonneau was employed to trade with the Kansas Indians. One day a man came there expecting to see one of the owners of the company. Finding he must wait for that gentleman's return, he spent a few days watching what took place among the traders. He learned that Charbonneau, his wife Sacajawea, who was the Indian girl guide for the Lewis and Clark Expedition, as well as her son, whom she had carried as a baby on her back, were in the settlement. He was delighted and sought them out.

He told them he was Prince Paul of Württemberg and had come in a ship across the Great Water from Hamburg, Germany, to New Orleans. He was a young man and although he had received a military training he had hated the life and chosen to study botany and zoology. The search for material had brought him to the New World and he had become fascinated with the life of an explorer. He had heard of the famous Lewis and Clark Expedition and he thought it a rare piece of good luck that he had found Sacajawea at the settlement. He had papers from the United States Government giving him permission to enter the country, and a passport from Captain Clark permitting him to go up the Missouri River.

All this did not impress Sacajawea. There were many who made expeditions up the river. But when Baptiste explained to her that this man had crossed the Great Water she was amazed. She had always believed the Great Water would stop the white man, but now she

knew that nothing would stop him. Her interest in the
stranger grew. He was from the hilltops beyond the
Great Water.

Prince Paul was very interested in the boy Baptiste.
He had a good knowledge of French and a fair knowledge of English and in addition could speak several
Indian languages. He liked the boy and it occurred to
him that it would be an interesting experiment to take
this youth with him to Germany when he returned. The
lad could tell his people many things that he could not.
He could continue Baptiste's education and, should he
decide to return again to America, the lad would be
valuable to him as friend, interpreter, and guide. He
decided to make the offer.

When he asked permission to take Baptiste with him
he explained his plan very carefully. He feared the boy's
mother would refuse, but it seemed too wonderful an
opportunity to be denied and she gave her consent.
Baptiste had planned to leave school and go with his
father, but this would open a new world for him and he
would have opportunities of education. Perhaps when he
came home, she reasoned, he would be a great man
who would know how to help their people. When Prince
Paul left them to go on his journey up the Missouri it
was settled that Baptiste would join him on his return
to Europe. Prince Paul kept a diary and that night he
wrote an account of their meeting and of the plan to
take Baptiste with him when he returned to Germany.
But Sacajawea could not sleep that night, for something
was crying within her. She had given her word and she
would keep it. Baptiste should go. But what would hap-

pen to her? What would there be to live for? She held
out her arms in the darkness and folded them to her
breast as she whispered, "I always wanted to hold you
right here, my little Pomp, my papoose."

Charbonneau went again as an interpreter and returned with a new wife, a member of the Ute tribe. She
was young and meant to rule his household. When she
met Charbonneau's other wives she knew that she would
have no trouble with Eagle, but she immediately resented Sacajawea's attractiveness and that something
she possessed which was more than mere beauty. She
resolved to settle at once and for all time her place
among the squaws while she was still the favored one
with Charbonneau. The fact that it was not easy to
entrap Sacajawea in an unfair act goaded her until she
deliberately forced a quarrel. She had chosen a day
when Baptiste and Toussaint were away. She raised her
voice and made a great scene, accusing Sacajawea of
mistreating her and begging Charbonneau to come to
her defense. He had long bottled up his resentment
against Sacajawea's independent ways, so the cries of
his new wife caused him to throw discretion to the
winds and vent his wrath upon her.

As his blows fell Sacajawea bowed before them but
made no cry. To be beaten was bad, but to be humiliated
before another wife was worse. When his anger had
spent itself he stepped back. There was silence for a
moment. The smile of triumph faded from the young
squaw's face and left a vacant expression that widened
into fear. Even Charbonneau shrank back as Sacajawea's
blazing eyes turned upon him. He had never seen her

like this before. She took a step toward him and seemed
to tower above him. He saw in her face the hate she had
held back for so long in her loyalty to him as his wife.
She despised him! And suddenly he feared her for the
first time. He remembered that she was young—young
and strong—and he was an old man. Sacajawea was the
first to turn away. Without a word she left them.

Charbonneau stumbled to a bench and drew a
wrinkled old hand across his brow. He wondered if
Captain Clark would hear of this. How had he been so
foolish as to forget himself? He dreaded the time when
Baptiste and Toussaint would return. They would guess
what had happened even if he did not tell them. He
looked at his young squaw. She raised her sullen face.

"Go for her," she said. "Drag her back. You did not
beat her enough!"

He shook his head. "It's no good. She will never come
back."

The girl shrugged an impudent shoulder. Suddenly
Charbonneau rose and turned upon her. "You are to
blame for all this. You drove her away. Get to work," he
bellowed. "There is much to be done. Have Eagle tell
you what to do."

Frightened, she scurried out to find Eagle who had
overheard all that had taken place and who gave the
young squaw the heaviest and hardest of tasks.

When the two boys returned and found Sacajawea
gone they knew that there had been trouble. They were
so infuriated when they had wrung the confession from
their father that they could have killed him. But the im-

portant thing now was to find their mother. They would know how to deal with Charbonneau later.

Sacajawea did not think where she was going, only that it should be away—as far away as possible. As her mind cleared she realized that if Charbonneau should overtake her there would be no limit to his punishment. He would not come empty-handed. She must find a place to hide until darkness came, when it would be safe to go on. She came to a stream and waded for some distance. A lush growth of bushes and vines shrouded the banks and at last she found a hiding place where vines clambered over a boulder near the water. She was so exhausted that she fell asleep quickly. She wakened suddenly. Someone was near. She lay motionless, scarcely breathing. Then she heard voices and she knew! Baptiste and Toussaint had come in search of her. They leaned against the great boulder that sheltered her.

"I do not wish to find her," said Baptiste. "He could even beat her to death for running away. There is no punishment too great. And, even though he says he did not lay a hand on her, how could she go back and live with that bad squaw he has just brought home? We cannot do that to her. She would rather be dead."

"You are right," said Toussaint. "She has been good to me. I could never take her back to Charbonneau. Do you think she will go south? Or will she try to go back to her people?"

"I hope she will go south," said Baptiste. "Life is easier there. She knows how to take care of herself and she always knows she can go back to St. Louis and that Captain Clark will help her."

"But she will never do that," said Toussaint. "She has always been loyal to Charbonneau and has never complained against him no matter how cruel he has been to her."

"We'll stay here awhile and then go back and tell him we could not find her," said Baptiste. "We'll watch Charbonneau. I hope he stays here for some time. I can't—" He paused as if unable to speak for a moment and then he added, "I can't think what life will be without her."

From her hiding place Sacajawea could almost touch them. Did they know she was there? Was this their farewell to her? She wanted to speak to them, but it was better that she did not. They could tell Charbonneau they had not found her. If she showed them where the lash had broken the flesh they would return and vent their wrath upon the old man, and that could make trouble for them all. For the last time these three were close together as they had been in the little log cabin. She heard them leave and listened to the direction of their footsteps. Then she was on her way toward the south country.

When daylight came she was rested and refreshed. All bitterness and resentment were gone and she seemed filled with a strange new joy! She was free, free, free! Charbonneau's blows had not broken her spirit but only her bonds. Now she was separated from him forever! She thought of Baptiste. He would soon be going with Prince Paul. She watched a mother bird pushing a timid baby out on a branch of a tree. It was time he learned to fly. She smiled to herself. Her little bird would be

153

flying. The time had to come, she told herself. She had done all she could for him and now he must fend for himself. Toussaint, too, could take care of himself. She was still young, and she would find a new life and this time it would be a better one. So she set out once more and the old eagerness came to her as she neared the first hilltop!

She found so much joy in following the trails, from standing on new hilltops, in drifting from place to place. She met Indians of other tribes and sometimes spent a few days with them. From her inquiries they believed she was looking for some of her people, so they told her of neighboring bands and of their friends and enemies. Soon she had a fair knowledge of the surrounding country and of the people she might meet as she went on her way. She loved the sun and the wind and as she walked she often loosened her long black braids to let the wind blow through her hair. The old days with Charbonneau seemed very far away. When the wild geese flew, as fall came on, she wondered if Baptiste had gone with Prince Paul and she knew a great longing to see him again.

And so the world changed for them all. Charbonneau found that in losing Sacajawea he had lost his two sons, for neither of them ever lived with him again. Baptiste and Toussaint found work for themselves and in the fall Baptiste made ready to go with Prince Paul as had been planned.

Six years later when he returned again with Prince Paul to St. Louis, he sought his mother but without success.

Chapter 17

Life with the Comanches

She wandered for a long time among many people and at last she came to the camp of the Comanches. A trader had come into the settlement and was engaged in bartering with the Indians for their furs. Sacajawea listened. The trader was a Frenchman and he offered them only a fraction of what their furs were worth. She knew Char-

155

bonneau drove a hard bargain with the Indians but not as hard as this. When she saw that the Indians were about to accept the offer she could stand it no longer. She stepped forward and spoke in French to the trader.

"You offer them too little. These are good skins. They are worth more."

He was startled. A squaw speaking to him in such a manner, and in French! He turned on her angrily and said to the Indians, "Take her away. I did not come to deal with squaws."

She spoke quietly to the Indians. "He is cheating you," she said. "I come from far away and I know the worth of furs. These are good. He will pay you more."

They were amazed! The squaw not only spoke in a strange tongue but also spoke their own language, so they told her to bargain for them. She secured double what they had first been offered. From that time they made her welcome and gave her a place to live. She learned that this tribe, the Comanches, had been a branch of the great Shoshone nation, as were her people in the Lemhi Valley. They had been driven south by the same tribes that had driven her people to seek refuge in the mountains. They still had many of the same ways and spoke the same language, but the Comanches had become more warlike and waged almost constant war especially on the people farther south.

There was a great deal of curiosity about the newcomer, for they wanted to know so much about her and she would tell so little. Because she was attractive and especially because one of their finest warriors, Jerk Meat, found her so, there came to be much gossip among the squaws. Jerk Meat was young and brave, a great warrior, loved and respected by his people. He asked Sacajawea about herself and for a moment she thought back over the years. There was so much to tell, but sticks and stones would speak against you and so would idle words. She would leave no trace; the past was a closed book. She shook her head as she answered, "I cannot. The past is gone like the winter when spring comes again."

Jerk Meat did many things to make life easier for her and she came to trust and respect him. When he asked her to become his squaw she told him, "When the white man takes a wife they are 'married.' The Captains—" She stopped suddenly and then went on, "I heard it once, although I did not know the words. They read it from a book. It was a promise. I would like to be married like a white squaw. The white squaw marries because she wishes to, not because she is sold. I come to you because I trust you. You pay nothing for me."

He listened. She was different from anyone he had known. Where had she been to learn all these things? But it was her secret and she should keep it. "I will say the words," he said, "if you will tell me."

"I promise," said Sacajawea.

"I promise," said Jerk Meat, and in their minds they were married in the white man's way as surely as if the Captain had read the words they could not understand.

They knew twenty-five happy years together. He was proud of her for her grace and beauty but most of all for her intelligence, and she had pride in his strength, courage, and understanding. There were children, five of them, but only Ticannof, the oldest, and Yoga-wasier (Crying Basket), the child of her later years, lived past infancy. She did not forget Baptiste. He was always in her thoughts. He held his place in her heart that no other child could take. Only when she was alone would she raise her arms as if reaching for him and draw him to her breast, whispering, "I always wanted to hold you right here."

Once Jerk Meat overheard her voice but not her words. "What did you say?" he asked.

"It was my heart speaking," she answered, and he knew it was from her past and asked no more.

Chapter 18

The Return to Her People

One day the news came that Jerk Meat had been killed in battle. He would never again come home to her! Sacajawea's little world crumbled about her. As she grieved for her husband and the days of happiness they would never again share together, there rose within her a great longing. Her husband had gone to some far place and she could not follow him. Now she would go. Something within her would not let her rest. She had forgotten many things in her years of contentment. There was no longer need for her to stay, now that her son had his own home. It did not occur to her that she was too old to go on such a long journey, for she carried her sixty years lightly.

She told her husband's people that she could not stay, but they did not believe her. One early morning she thought she heard a call—the call of the wild geese. It was a sign to her, so she made ready a small parfleche bag and filled it with dried buffalo meat and, with her daughter, she left the Comanche settlement. Walking seemed to ease something within her and she found herself hurrying to reach the first hilltop. Another chapter of her life had ended, but she faced with eagerness what lay ahead. Her husband's people found a great heap of brush piled to the top of her lodge and they knew it meant she did not intend to return.

They sent for her son and he visited the neighboring tribes in the surrounding country, but no one had seen her. The Comanches said she was a strange woman—no one knew where she had come from nor where she had gone. They gave her a new name, Wadze-wipe, meaning Lost Woman.

Again Sacajawea's moccasined feet were following the trails. Sometimes she carried little Crying Basket when her legs grew tired. Sometimes they both sat and rested. There was plenty of time. They could enjoy the hilltops.

She went on and on. People were her friends wherever she went. When the white men learned she had been with Lewis and Clark they gave her a lift on their wagon trains or gave her a horse to ride. Sometimes she stopped for a long time—all winter if she was made welcome—

before she again started on her journey. Always she traveled to the northwest and asked all she met, "Have you seen Baptiste, Baptiste Charbonneau?" And she told them, "The white man is our friend. We can learn from him how to raise our food and stop the suffering our people have known. His ways are good. Let us keep peace with him."

She said it over and over at many campfires as she made her way across the miles and through the long years of her pilgrimage. Crying Basket grew and came to be a help to her and no longer a burden as the two went on together.

One day Sacajawea found a man who could answer her question, "Have you seen Baptiste?" He was an old trapper.

"Baptiste, Baptiste Charbonneau? I knew him well. That fellow just felt the mountains. He didn't even have to see 'em! It was uncanny, I'm telling you. Never was a guide like him. He just seemed to know by instinct, I guess, where there was a pass. There was Captain Cook, who took him to help map out wagon trails in the southwest. He told me himself that he never could have done it without Charbonneau—that's Baptiste Charbonneau. I guess his father was a pretty good interpreter but not so good as Baptiste. For a guide Baptiste had everyone beat. Do you know him?" he asked suddenly. "He is a breed—father a Frenchman and mother an Indian. Short fellow, and quiet."

"That is Baptiste," she answered. "Where is he?"

"Think I heard that he was at Fort Bridger."

161

"Fort Bridger?" asked Sacajawea. "Where is Fort Bridger?"

"That's where Jim Bridger has his blacksmith shop. Jim's an old-timer. He knows that country like a book. Been there a long time. It's on the headwaters of the Green River this side of the mountains on the Oregon Trail."

"Bazil?" asked Sacajawea. "Do you know Bazil?"

"Bazil? He's there too. Same place as Charbonneau. Mighty white Indian, Bazil."

"You know Toussaint?" she questioned.

He shook his head. "Never heard of him."

Fort Bridger, Oregon Trail—a country changes in half a lifetime. Even names were strange to her. Out on the trail she saw some wagons coming. When they drew near, a driver called, "Want a ride?" He could not pass an old squaw and a young girl so far from any settlement.

"Where are you going?" she asked.

"Fort Bridger." And before he knew it they were both scrambling up over the wheel, glad to have a ride the last long miles.

She found her people, as the old trapper said she would, in the Bridger Valley. As she walked through the tent village she saw no one she knew.

"Where is Baptiste?" she asked. "Where is Bazil?"

They pointed out Bazil's lodge. Baptiste, they said, was away. When at last she found Bazil and explained who she was, he welcomed her as his mother and took her to his lodge. Crying Basket joined Bazil's children so that the two were alone to talk together.

It took a long time to tell only of the chief events of so many years. Bazil had often heard how she had returned with the white Captains and adopted him over forty years ago as was the Indian custom. He tried to tell her the story of her people. Cameahwait had been a brave and good Chief; but they had led a troubled life, continually being harassed by their enemies. He had been killed while fighting bravely some ten years before and Bazil had done his best to keep their people together. Other small bands of Shoshones were having the same difficulty and when a wise and brave leader, Chief Washakie, had arisen they had all rallied under his leadership. Bazil was an under-chief, close friend and adviser. She glowed with pride as he told the story and then she asked the question so close to her heart.

"Tell me of Baptiste."

A shadow passed over his face and he did not speak for a moment.

"He came here a long time ago," he said slowly. "He likes it here. He likes to hunt." He paused and added, "He likes to be alone."

Sacajawea would not be content without the story and before he left her he told her all he knew. Baptiste had been one of the best guides and interpreters in the west. All had seemed well with him until the fur trade began to decline. Then there was no longer the need for his services and there seemed to be nothing else he wished to do. When he first came to the valley he told strange stories and they laughed. Sacajawea nodded. She knew, for she remembered how they laughed at the story of the whale. Baptiste had talked of crossing the Great Water,

163

of "Big Houses on the Water" and of the "Wooden Shoe White Man!"

"I remember this," said Bazil. "They laughed and his words ceased like a stream that is frozen." He sighed. "He seems happy only when he is tramping through the mountains hunting or fishing."

After Bazil had left her she sat thinking. What had happened to her boy? The years, what had they done to him? Bazil had changed from a little child to a man well past middle age. It would almost be the same with Baptiste; the years would lie heavily upon him. She rose and went outside. There were the mountains! The mountains were the same; they did not change!

Baptiste came to see her when he returned. There was little of the youth she had known and loved. He was short and stocky as were her people and his face was deeply tanned and weather-beaten. For a moment they stood looking at one another trying to cross the gap of years that lay between them.

"My Baptiste," she said, "how many summers have I lost?" She was straight and strong, only her graying hair showed the passing years. They sat together for a long time in silence.

"You have talked with Bazil," he said at last.

"He has told much of what has happened to our people," said Sacajawea.

"And of me?"

"You shall tell me that," she answered.

"I will tell you. Once there was a weasel. He was brown. When winter came all his brothers turned white; then they were ermine. But this weasel did not turn all white. Half of him was still brown. In summer when all his brothers were brown he was still half white. He felt strange. It was as if he were not a weasel nor an ermine. So he would go away by himself. As he could not be like them he was not happy with them." He paused.

Sacajawea waited for a long time. "I understand," she said slowly, "but if the weasel had forgotten he was different from the others they soon would have forgotten too. I might be a weasel. I have lived with the brown weasels and the white ermine. I have liked them both and they have been my friends. I do not feel that I am better than the brown weasel or poorer than the ermine. I have learned from the ermine, but I have never turned white. Be proud, my son, of what you are."

He put his head in his hands. "I wanted to be a great man. Everything I did I tried to do better than others. Then the end came. There was nothing. Bazil is a leader. Bazil cannot read or write. What is the matter with me?"

"Bazil thinks not of being great; he thinks only of his people," said his mother. "Remember Bazil has lived with them all his life and they know and trust him. You can help Bazil. He is a loyal brother to you."

They sat, each thinking his own thoughts, and then Baptiste rose to go. "I am glad you have come," he said simply. "I can talk to you."

She watched him go, and as he disappeared from sight she held out her arms in the old gesture and whispered, "Oh, my Baptiste, I always wanted to hold you right here."

She knew it would take time for him to open the doors of his heart and mind, which had been closed for so long. One day he would talk to her and tell her of his trip across the Great Water and of the many exciting experiences he had known upon the mountain trails. And something warmed within her—it was well she had come; he needed her!

Chapter 19

Life on the Reservation

In the months following her return Sacajawea studied her people and found that a great change had taken place. They no longer ran from their enemies; they defended themselves and they did not seek warfare. Now they had a reputation for fearlessness and bravery which warring tribes of far greater numbers had come to respect.

"We have a great Chief named Washakie," the older people told her. "He knows both the Indian's and the white man's ways of battle, so he can outfight either of them," they added proudly.

"Tell me about him," said Sacajawea.

"He came to us when a small boy the age of Bazil. His mother was a Shoshone and his father a Flathead. His father had been killed, so his mother came here with her children. Later she returned, but Washakie stayed with us in the Lemhi Valley. He became a great hunter and went with the white trappers and traders. He learned to speak their language. He is their friend and has made a vow that he will never go to war against the white man."

"He is wise," nodded Sacajawea. "The white man is moving in. Nothing can stop him—the winds, the storms, the river, or the Great Water. The white-top wagons are to be found on every road across the land, for a change is coming to both the white man and the Indian. He will take our lands and make his living from them. The game will be gone and we must learn his ways if we are to live. Our Chief is wise. He will lead us safely. The old days are gone, but there is a better new day ahead for us."

She knew they did not understand. She would tell them, she thought, bit by bit, of the things she had seen, to prepare them for what lay ahead.

She still loved to follow the trails and when the longing came to her she put everything aside and, on the horse her sons had given her, she followed trail and stream visiting friendly people and carrying her message of good will: "The white man's ways are good; let us be at peace with him."

She found friends among both the whites and the Indians. When she decided to ride the stage the drivers would take no pay for her fare.

"You earned your fare with Lewis and Clark," they said gruffly. Kindness always touched her deeply and she would say her thanks in French, thinking, "The brown weasel and the ermine are all my friends."

But she loved best to ride through the trails edged by the great pines with the blue of the sky overhead. When she reached an open park, sitting straight in the saddle, she would loosen her hair and give it to the wind and even her mount would feel the joy she knew as he carried her with flying feet. It was almost as if she recaptured the joyous days of her girlhood when, riding double, she and Rabbit Ear followed the trails together.

One day she made a travois to carry bundles to and from the post at Fort Bridger. Her moccasins always found a ready sale with trappers and traders who came there, for she had become so skillful that they declared the skins wore out leaving intact the threads of sinew that bound them together! She wondered as she worked what the white women would do if they had to make such a thing for themselves.

Baptiste came to see her more and more often, although it was still difficult for him to express himself even to her. Sometimes they sat together through the twilight scarcely speaking but knowing the contentment of being together. Little by little she came to know more about the years of their separation.

"Washakie is a great chieftain," he told her. "I will fight wherever he leads. I am not a leader. I am a warrior. I am not afraid."

"Do you know of your brother Toussaint?" she asked him.

He shook his head. "When I was across the Great Water he grew away from me. When I returned we were strangers. He had changed into another person. He was like the sky, smiling and sunny, that can change into a tempest and destroy everything before it." He paused for a moment. "He was often in trouble. I have heard he was killed in a fight. I do not know."

For a long time Sacajawea sat thinking. Toussaint was more like his father than Baptiste. Even as a boy he had been willful, hot-tempered, and boastful. A great thankfulness rose up within her for her son Baptiste. It did not matter that he was not a leader as she had dreamed he might sometime be. Making marks on paper and reading from a book could not make one a great man. Captain Clark was mistaken. Baptiste was not meant to be a leader. Baptiste was her son. He knew the mountains as she had known them. And now that he was a warrior he would be a good one, she told herself, and contentment concerning him came to her at last.

One day Bazil brought Chief Washakie to see her. He was a splendid-looking man, tall, dignified, and, she thought, every inch a chieftain!

"Your son Bazil has told me of you," he said in French. "You have been to far places. You have lived among the lodges of the white man. You know much that you can tell to our people. Your son has given me your words, 'The white man is our friend. Let us be at peace with him!' Those are my words."

She nodded. He went on. "I have a dream—a dream

of a home for our people, where they may have good hunting and fishing while the game lasts and where they may learn to till the soil as do the Mormons who live to the west of us."

"I have seen them," said Sacajawea. "They settled by the Great Salt Lake not long before I returned. They make magic with the water they bring from the streams. The barren lands become fruitful without rain."

"It is so," said the Chief. "We shall learn to do it too. I am asking the Great Father in Washington to give us this new home."

There seemed to be no doubt in the Chief's mind that the Great Father had the right to give them the land, for the Indian creed had always been "Might makes right." One could only own land if he could defend it; otherwise it would be taken from him. The Chief had confidence that they could hold the land with the government's aid, for without it they would be at the mercy of the Sioux, the Cheyenne, and other enemy tribes.

"A home for our people," repeated Sacajawea. "But this is our home. Our people have lived here for many years."

"Each year there is less game," said the Chief. "The 'white tops' keep coming and our root lands will become their fields. If we give this land to the white men I believe they will give us a reservation in the warm valleys of the Wind River. It is a wonderful place. The animals have gone there, for it is away from the white man's trails. It is the place for us. Soon we can learn to raise crops like the white men."

"It sounds good," said Sacajawea.

"The white men have something new," the Chief went on. "It is coming to us here. It is a new trail—a trail for their Fire Horse. When the Fire Horse comes it will frighten the animals."

"What is it?" asked Sacajawea eagerly.

"It is something the white men have made. It is very large and breathes fire. Smoke comes from its nostrils. It can pull heavy loads."

"Is it alive?" asked Sacajawea.

"It seems to be, but it is not. It must stay on the trail they are making for it. I do not understand it."

"Perhaps it is like the steamboat. I saw the first one on the Mississippi. It carried heavy loads up and down the river by itself without help. There was no sail and there were no oars. Steam made it go. The fire heated water and made steam. My boys learned about it in school. The white men harnessed the steam and made it work for them. And now they have harnessed it again, only they do not use the oars or sail or even the river. They make a trail instead of the river for it to travel upon." She shook her head in wonder. "White man's magic," she said.

"No," said the Chief, "no. It is not magic. The white men's minds are in the light and ours have been in darkness. But we will find the light. First we must lead our people to desire the things that are good for them. I do not wish to drive them. The new home must be something we all wish to have. You can help me, for you have seen much and you know the things I tell you are true."

Sacajawea could hardly believe his words. She could help him, the great Chief! He saw the light come into her face as she promised to do all she could. Life had a new meaning to her now. She had a task to do. There was a goal ahead, but before it lay a long hard hill to climb. But such a reward when she reached the top!

Nor was it to be accomplished in a short time. It took years of patience and understanding, but at last the thing that once seemed so impossible lost its strangeness and came to be something to be desired. The time might have come sooner had not the white men known difficulties among their own people between the north and the south. The great disturbance could not fail to cause widening ripples that reached across the land. Until this was ended less important things were forced to wait. But at last Chief Washakie, after years of faithfulness and loyalty to the whites and their government, was to be rewarded by the granting of his long-cherished desire. The time they had longed for at last had come! Sacajawea had known moments when she had been fearful she might not live to see the new home to which her people were going, for she was at least eighty years of age when the orders came from General Augur for them to assemble at Fort Bridger.

Chief Washakie brought his people with him and they set up their village of skin tepees near by. The General held conferences with the leaders explaining all details of the treaty whereby they would relinquish their present home to the government for the new one their chieftain desired.

On July 3, 1869, a great council was held with all the tribe in attendance, the officers and soldiers at the Fort, and other government officers interested in Indian affairs. Captain Augur spoke through an interpreter and the Chief spoke of his desires for his people if they accepted the new home he had secured for them, and then he called on Sacajawea to speak.

For a moment she did not think she could, for there were so many faces turned toward her—friendly faces, white and brown—but she remembered this was for her people. She stood before them, a little figure slender and straight, her face lined by more than eighty summer suns, and her hair quite gray. But her voice was steady and her earnestness held her listeners' attention.

"In the warm days our Chief prepares for the cold days. In the days of plenty he prepares for the days of hunger. Today he thinks of tomorrow. Shall we wait and see if the game is frightened away and our root lands gone? No, we are not blind. We have seen these things coming closer day by day. Our Chief knows our needs. We can trust him. He knows when it is time to stay and when it is time to go. Let us not look back; let us look forward. So much lies ahead for us."

Her words were received with approval from her people. The "Great Treaty" was signed the following day, July 4, 1869, by Washakie and his subchiefs—among them Bazil, Sacajawea's adopted son—thus creating the Shoshone Indian Reservation in Wyoming, which twenty-one days later was made a territory by an act of Congress. But Washakie and his people did not go at once to live upon the new reservation.

"Why do we not go?" asked his people.

"We need protection," he told them. "Our enemies will annihilate us. The Great Father has promised to build an agency and send troops. We must give him time to keep his promises."

"Why do you not go?" asked the white man at Fort Bridger.

"We must have protection," said the Chief. "You want us to help protect the gold fields at our southern border. It is filled with white men with no protection. We cannot do this alone. Build the fort you promised and send in troops and then we will go."

"The Chief is wise," Sacajawea told Bazil when they talked together.

"But our people are restless and are becoming discontent."

"We must wait for the good things," said his mother. "The grass springs up quickly and is gone. The tree grows slowly but lives a lifetime. Our reservation is worth waiting for. What good will it do us if we go before it is safe to go and are killed?"

She talked to her people and begged them to be patient, but when she heard the call of the wild geese she knew a longing she found hard to restrain.

They were still in the Bridger Valley when the Fire Horse came rushing by on its tie and rail "trail." The whole tribe stood and watched as the little engine "huffed and puffed" with rattle and roar as it pulled its loaded cars behind it, the smoke belching from its smokestack. Some of the children cried and had to be assured that it could not leave its trail and chase them, and many of their elders felt relief when the monster disappeared from sight. But most of them stood in silence, even Chief Washakie, for they could find no words to express their wonder.

At last the government established an agency with a fort and troops to protect it and Chief Washakie led his people to their new home. Sacajawea was given a log house to live in, but she loved her skin tepee better. They did not expect that life would be peaceful, for the Indian spent his life hunting and fighting. When enemies attacked them they rode out against them. Around their campfires, stories were told of their battles just as they had been told for generations among her people.

The "Great Father in Washington" sent trained men to help them learn the white man's way of raising crops, and in this Chief Washakie, Bazil, and Sacajawea gave them much encouragement. But progress was slow and results often discouraging. It would take time, Sacajawea came to understand, to teach her people their new ways of life. Sometimes she wondered about herself. Why did she care? Was she different? And she remembered the days of her desperation in the camp of the Minataree when she realized she was no longer like her people, or the Mandan or the Minataree, and wondered what she had become. She was still a brown weasel, she told herself, and she must use the things she had learned to help them.

"My winters and summers are becoming a heavy load," she thought sometimes, "but I still have much to do." One day Bazil and Baptiste came to see her.

"We are going to buffalo," they told her.

"When?" she asked eagerly. "I must make ready."

They shook their heads. "We dare not take you. We

will pitch your tepee near the agent's house and the agent's wife will look after you while we are away."

She looked into their faces and she knew. They thought she was an old, old squaw. So she was not going on the hunt! She would be left behind! Panic possessed her. Where were the trails? Where were the hilltops? Would she never find them again? She dared not try to speak for fear they would know she had read their thoughts.

That night she sat alone in her tepee. They were far away. Perhaps now they were making ready their festivities. She could see the great fires they would build and hear the voices of the medicine men chanting their rituals to drive away evil spirits, and the low drone of the drums beating. And suddenly she knew that she did not need to follow the trails for new hilltops. Her mind was a storehouse of them! It was as if she were with her people. On the morrow, she told herself, she would go with them to the hunt as she sat in her tepee!

The agent's wife found her quite content. She asked Sacajawea to teach her to speak Shoshone and to tell her of her life. The two women spent many hours together as Sacajawea followed the trails and climbed the hilltops in telling the story of her days with Lewis and Clark so long ago. Sometimes she thought of the old, old squaw of her childhood who had so few comforts of life and she was thankful for her two sons near her and for Crying Basket, who was grown and had her own home on the reservation. She often thought of her life with Jerk Meat and the happy years they had known together, and of their son, Ticannof, who lived in Oklahoma among his father's people, the Comanches. She longed to see him and told herself that some day when she was stronger she would make the long journey again.

She grew to be very old, far into her nineties, but she clung to her independence and defied the burden of her years. One April night she watched the tent flap of the sky open to receive the setting sun and saw the dusky shadows come stealing in to wrap the mountains in the purple robes of night. She loved this quiet hour at the end of the day, for it was always a time for remembering. She smoothed her fringed buckskin dress with a wrinkled hand. "How comfortable it is!" she thought. "And my moccasins have been my wings, for they have carried me up and over so many hilltops! Hilltops! Hilltops are desires that one yearns for, works for, sacrifices for. The white men have hilltops too. After all, we are alike."

A bit of red, white, and blue cloth fluttering from a staff on the shores of the Great Water was the hilltop the Captains sought. Her mind moved on down the Missouri. Mountains of furs were the hilltops of so many in St. Louis. The farmer's hilltop for which he worked was the harvest. On the Oregon Trail in the "white tops" came those whose hilltop was a new home in the west. For the thousands who came on horseback, in wagons, and even on foot to South Pass and Atlantic City just south of the reservation, their hilltop was gold! Chief Washakie had won his hilltop when he had secured the reservation, but he was not content; he still climbed seeking a better life for his people.

What were her people's hilltops? For generations it had been a successful hunt or victory over an enemy.

But now that the great herds were almost gone and trouble with enemy tribes was growing less, they needed to find new goals. Surely some day they would awaken to new desires and begin to climb. Then they, too, would know the joy that came from reaching the top of a hill, even a small hill, that one has worked to climb. She must help them—she must share her knowledge of hilltops with them. There was so much still to be done, she told herself. She rose stiffly and, drawing her blanket about her, turned toward her cabin. She wished she were not so old and that Jerk Meat were there to help her. He would understand and know how to carry out her plan. He was young and strong in the land beyond the sunset and some day when she climbed a very steep hill she would find him!

She found her shakedown and made herself comfortable in her blankets. They were so warm and the hard floor rested her. She slept peacefully. But as she dreamed, perhaps she heard the call of the wild geese and it roused all the old desire and yearning she had known through all her lifetime. But this time she answered them joyously. At last nothing held her back, for her great spirit stripped away the feeble bonds that bound it and found that it, too, had wings.

IN MEMORY

Sacajawea lies buried in the Shoshone Indian Reservation Cemetery at Wind River, Wyoming, in the shadow of the snow-capped mountains that she knew as friends. The Reverend John Roberts, Episcopal Missionary to her people, conducted a Christian burial service for her.

Every year many people come to pay tribute to the memory of this woman who made two great contributions to our country. Her part as guide in the Lewis and Clark Expedition is the best known, but quite as important and perhaps of even greater value were her efforts through many years of her life to promote understanding and peaceful relations between the white men and her people.

A simple cement stone column marks her grave bearing a bronze tablet with this inscription:

Sacajawea
Died April 9, 1884
A Guide With The
Lewis and Clark Expedition
1805-1806
Identified 1908 by Rev. J. Roberts
Who Officiated At Her Burial

Bibliography

Bancroft, Hubert Howe, *History of the Northwest Coast.*
　　San Francisco, The History Company, 1890

Chittendon, Hiram Martin, *The American Fur Trade of the Far West.* New York, F. P. Harper, 1902

Cook, Philip St. George, Whiting and Aubrey, *Exploring Southwestern Trails.* Glendale, California, Arthur H. Clark Co., 1938

Defenbach, Byron, *Red Heroines of the Northwest.*
　　Caldwell, Idaho, The Caxton Printers, 1929

Hebard, Dr. Grace Raymond, *Sacajawea.* Glendale, California, Arthur H. Clark Co., 1933

Washakie. Cleveland, Ohio, Arthur H. Clark Co., 1930

Lewis and Clark, *Original Journals of the Lewis and Clark Expedition, 1804–1806,* 8 vols. New York, Dodd Mead and Co., 1904–1905

Index

Augur, General, 173

Baptiste, son of Sacajawea and Charbonneau, birth of, 67-68; Capt. Clark's interest in, 68, 71, 87, 117, 120, 127-29, 133-35; dilemma of, 163-66, 169; as interpreter, 161, 163; and men of Expedition, 70-71, 88, 95, 113; and Prince Paul of Württemberg, 149, 153; reunion with mother, 164-66

Bare feet ritual, 93

Barter system, 86-87, 138

Bazil, adopted son of Sacajawea, 105, 144, 162-64, 170, 174

Bear hunt, the, 80-82

Beaverhead River, 94, 125

Bismarck, North Dakota, camp of the Minataree Indians near, 39

Bitter Root, 105

Blackfeet Indians, land of, 84

"Blanket" tradition, 31, 60, 92, 97, 99

Bozeman Pass, 126

Bratton, hunter and gunsmith on Expedition, 80, 87-88

Bridger, Jim, 162

Bridger Valley, 175

British fur traders, 142

Brown weasel and white ermine, symbol of, 164-65, 169, 176

Buffalo hunt, 28-32, 176

Cameahwait, brother of Sacajawea, and bond with sister, 31; bravery of, 34-35, 163; as chief of tribe, 44, 60; as hunter, 18, 19-20, 28-29; and reunion with Sacajawea, 97-98, 105

Ceremonial garments, description of, 27

Charbonneau, Toussaint, 47, 48; and bargain with Capt. Clark, 130, 134-35, 146, 151; as Expedition interpreter, 56-61, 76, 86, 101, 108, 132; as interpreter for traders, 132, 140, 161; and interview with Lewis and Clark, 55-61; and new squaws, 145, 150-51; and Sacajawea's departure from, 151; settles in St. Louis, 133-34, 140; takes Sacajawea as wife, 48-49; and trade with Mandan Indians, 46-50; tells Sacajawea about Christmas, 65-67; and termination of Expedition, 127; and treatment of Sacajawea, 49, 50, 52, 77-78, 115, 120, 146, 147, 150-51, 153-54; and "white man's marriage," 63-64

Cheyenne Indians, 171

Chief of Shoshone Indians, father of Sacajawea, 15, 18, 27, 28; death of, 34; sells Sacajawea to Little Wolf, 29-31, 100-03

Christmas Day, during Expedition, 65-66, 112

Christ, story of, 65-66, 112

Civil War, United States (1861-65), 173

Clapsop Indians, 108, 109

Clark, Capt. William (1770-1838), 53; and appreciation of Sacajawea, 82-83, 99, 113, 129-30, 134, 143; and help to Charbonneau's family, 130, 133-35,

Clark, Capt. William (cont'd)
146, 151; homeward route of,
125; and interest in Baptiste,
117, 120, 127-29, 133-34, 135;
and interest in Sacajawea as
guide, 56-61; learns Indian
words from Sacajawea, 75-76;
Sacajawea's faith in, 87, 119,
140; on Sacajawea's heroism,
82-83

Clearwater River, Indian village
on, 124

"Colter's Hell," 88

Colter, John, 82; first man to see
Yellowstone Park, 88

Columbia River, 106; site of fort,
107

Comanche Indians, 11; Sacajawea
among, 155-58

Cook, Captain James (1728-79),
161

Coronado, Francisco Vasquez de
(1500-1554), 85

Council meeting, Indian (July 3,
1869), 173-74

Covered wagons, and expansion
to West, 168, 171, 178

Cruzatte, Peter, 64, 81, 82, 88,
90, 91, 112, 117

Crying Basket, daughter of Sacajawea, 158, 160, 161, 162, 177

Dalles, The, 106, 123

Drewyer, 81

Drouillard, 88, 92, 94

Eagle, wife of Charbonneau, 145,
146, 147, 151

Eastman, Dr. Charles Alexander,
11, 12

England, people in St. Louis from,
136

Farming, as practiced by the
Minatarees, 41, 43

Field, Joseph, 88

Field, Reuben, 88

"Fire Horse," 172, 175-76

Flathead Indians, 168

Fort Bridger, 161-62, 169, 173

Fort Clatsop, wintering at, 109,
123, 138

France, land purchased from, 86,
136

Fur trading, 133, 136, 140, 141-
42, 147, 148, 155-56, 163

Fur-trapping, among Indians, 142,
155

Gallatin River, 125

Gass, Patrick, 54, 88, 90

Great Falls, of Missouri River, 84,
85, 86, 125, 126

Great Salt Lake, 171

"Great Treaty" (July 4, 1869),
174

Great Water. See Pacific Ocean

Green River, 162

Gros Ventres. See Minataree Indians

Hamburg, Germany, 148

Hebard, Dr. Grace Raymond, 11

Hilltops, symbol of, 14-15, 17-18,
37, 39, 42, 43, 46, 72, 115,
117, 133, 143, 149, 154, 160,
173, 177, 178

Indian agency, at Shoshone Indian Reservation, 176-77

Indian Reservation. See Shoshone
Wind River Reservation

Indian tribes. See Comanche Indians; Mandan Indians; Minataree Indians; Pahkee Indians;
Shoshone Indians; Snake Indian tribe

Irrigation, of land, 171
"Janey." *See* Sacajawea
Jefferson River, 90, 125, 126
Jefferson, Thomas, and Lewis and Clark Expedition, 55, 112; and Louisiana Purchase, 86
Jerk Meat, husband of Sacajawea, 156-58, 177; death of, 159
Kansas Indians, 148
Kaw River, 148
Knife River, 75, 84
Lemhi Pass, 23, 47, 104
Lemhi Valley, home of Shoshone Indians, 26, 41, 42, 44, 45, 47, 56, 144, 156
Lewis and Clark Expedition, 11; claims land for U. S., 92-93, 107; and celebration of Christmas, 64-65, 111-13; and departure from Mandan village, 73; and fort at Columbia River, 107-08; and hardships, 74-76, 84, 85-86, 105-06; and hunt for big bears, 80-83; and last stage of journey, 105, 106; meeting with Sacajawea's people, 96-97; and men's interest in Baptiste, 68, 71, 95, 128; and men's speculations on Sacajawea, 68-70; and parting with Sacajawea, 126; plan of, 53, 104; route of, 53-54, 73, 80-83, 84-85, 89-90, 92-94, 96-97, 104-07, 123, 124-25; and Sacajawea's heroism, 81-84; Sacajawea's role in, 69, 70, 74, 75, 77, 79, 82-84, 88, 90-92, 94, 96-99, 105, 108-10, 113, 119-21, 123-28, 148; sights Rocky Mountains, 84; and winter in Mandan village, 53-54

Lewis, Capt. Meriwether (1774-1809), 53; claims land for United States government, 92-93; homeward route of, 124-25; interest in Sacajawea as guide, 56-61; and praise of Sacajawea, 83-84, 98, 99, 129; Sacajawea's esteem of, 87; on scouting trip, 92; and Shoshone Indians, 93-94
Little Wolf, 29-31, 100-03, 139
Lolo River, 124
Louisiana Purchase, 86, 136
Madison River, 125
Mandan Indians, and Lewis and Clark Expedition, 53-73; life of, 42-45, 73, 129, 135
"Might makes right," creed of, 171
Milk River, 84
Minataree Indians, 11, 97; and Lewis and Clark Expedition, 87; life of, 39-42, 44, 45, 47, 84, 129
Mississippi River, 136, 141, 143; first steamboat on, 144-45
Missouri River, 31, 53, 84, 85, 120, 125, 126, 128, 134, 147
Money, meaning of, to Sacajawea, 86-87, 138, 144
Mormons, 171
Napoleon, and Louisiana Purchase, 86
Negro slaves, in St. Louis, 136, 139
New Orleans, La., 148
Oklahoma, home of Ticannof, 177
Oregon Trail, 162, 178
Otter Woman, wife of Charbonneau, 49, 52, 58, 61, 73, 127, 131, 132, 136, 138-40, 142, 143

Pacific Ocean, 92, 97, 112, 114, 138; end of Expedition trail, 104-07; Sacajawea sees, 116-17

Pahkee Indians, and attack on Shoshones, 33-35, 90; home of, 70, 84, 101

"Pale face," 43, 47, 100

"Papoose board," description of, 73

Paul Williams, Prince of Württemberg, 12, 148-49, 153, 154

"Pomp." *See* Baptiste

Rabbit Ear, friend of Sacajawea, 13-14, 16-18, 19, 36, 95, 99-100, 169

Railroad, new trail for, 172, 175

Reservation, Washakie's dream of, 171-72, 176

Roberts, Reverend John, 181

Rocky Mountains, 84, 86, 87, 92, 93

Sacajawea, becomes Charbonneau's wife, 48; and call of wild geese, 16-17, 24, 36-37, 43, 48, 50, 72, 100, 143, 163, 175, 179; death of, 179; description of, 60, 73, 76, 83, 90, 129-30, 146, 156, 157, 164, 169; and desire for knowledge, 17-18, 21-23, 48, 64-66, 76, 86, 107, 114-15, 138, 179; and end of Expedition, 126-27, 131; and first meeting with Expedition, 52; girlhood of, 15-32; gives birth to son, 67; grave of, 181; heroism of, 82-83; and interview with Clark and Lewis, 59-61; joins Expedition, 61; last days of, 176-79; learns about Christmas, 64-67; and life with Comanches, 155-58; and life with Minatarees, 39-48; and life in St. Louis, 133-54; and Little Wolf, 100-03; marries Jerk Meat, 157; and meaning of her name, 17; as a mother, 67-68, 71, 76, 87, 88, 95, 103, 110, 117-19, 127, 128-29, 133-34, 136, 143-44, 149-50, 152, 153-54, 157-58, 161-62, 164-66, 177; promotes understanding between white man and Indian, 161, 168, 170, 181; reminiscences of, 177-79; and reunion with her people (Lemhi Valley), 95-105 (Fort Bridger), 167; and reunion with her sons, 162-66, 169-70, 176; and role of, in Expedition, 69, 70, 74, 75, 77, 79, 82-84, 88, 90-92, 94, 96-99, 105, 108-10, 113, 119-21, 123-28, 148; and speech at Great Council, 174; and symbol of hilltops, 14-15, 17-18, 37, 39, 42, 43, 46, 72, 115, 117, 133, 143, 149, 154, 160, 173, 177, 178; and symbol of squash vines, 44, 51, 72, 117, 133; and talks with old squaw, 21-23, 86; taken prisoner, 35-37, 56; and tribute to her memory, 181; and "white man's" marriage ceremony, 63-64; and work for Indian Reservation, 170-74

Sacajawea Creek, 84

Salmon River, 105

St. Louis, Mo., Charbonneau and family settle in, 133; description of, 136-38, 140; and first steamboat, 145; fur market at, 133, 134; women in, 136-37

188

Scalp lock, 22, 33, 36

Shannon, George, 88, 90, 91

Shields, hunter and iron worker of Expedition, 88

Shoshone Indian Reservation cemetery, 181

Shoshone Indians (Lemhi Valley), 11, 123; attached by Pahkees, 33-35; and buffalo hunt, 28-32; life of, 15-16, 21-24, 26-32, 128, 163; and Snake Indian tribe, 21-22, 56; suspicious of white men, 56, 57

Shoshone Wind River Reservation, grave of Sacajawea in, 11; setting up of, 174

Sioux Indians, 11, 171

"Smoking sticks," 23, 34, 52, 59

Snake Indian tribe, 21-22, 56

Snake River, 106

Spain, 86, 136

"Squash vine," symbol of, 44, 51, 72, 117, 133

Squaw, status of, 16, 27, 30, 31, 41, 42, 50, 62-63, 77, 92, 96-97, 102, 103, 139, 140, 145, 146

Steamboat, first, on Mississippi, 145, 172

"Tabba-bone" (white man), meaning of, 92

Three Forks, 89, 125, 126

Ticannof, child of Sacajawea, 158, 177

Toussaint, son of Otter Woman, 49, 73, 127, 131, 143-44, 152-53, 170

Trading, with Indians, 43, 46-47, 147, 148

Trading posts, 136, 142, 148

U. S. Department of Indian Affairs, 11

United States, Expedition claims land for, 92-93, 107; and Louisiana Purchase, 136

University of Wyoming, 11

Ute Indians, 150

Vancouver, George (1758-98), 106

Wadze-wipe (Lost Woman), 160

Walla Walla Indians, 123

War of 1812, 142

Washakie, Chief of Shoshone, 163, 167-68, 169; and dream of, 170-72; and fulfillment of dream, 173, 174, 176, 178

Weasel tails, value of, 112-13

Whale, episode of, 114-17, 132, 163

White ermine and brown weasel, symbol of, 164-65, 169, 176

"White man's magic," 138, 140, 145, 157, 171, 172

"White man's marriage," 63-64, 139

"White squaws," 136-37, 139

"White tops." See Covered wagons, and expansion to West

Wild geese, symbol of, 16-17, 24, 36-37, 43, 48, 50, 72, 100, 143, 163, 175, 179

Wind River, Wyoming, 171, 181

Women, Indian, status of. See Squaw, status of

Women, in St. Louis, 136-37

Yellowstone Park, 88

Yellowstone River, 125, 126

Yoga-wasier. See Crying Basket

York, Negro servant of Capt. Clark, 68-69, 87, 105